Stagewise Process Design

Stagewise Process Design

ERNEST J. HENLEY AND

H. KENNETH STAFFIN

Stevens Institute of Technology

JOHN WILEY & SONS, INC., NEW YORK · LONDON · SYDNEY

◀ *Atmospheric pipestill fractionating column at Rasiom Refinery, Sicily. The 151-ft tall unit contains forty-seven 6-in. circular base caps and processes 55,000 B/SD of Raquasa crudes. Photo courtesy of Standard Oil Co. (N.J.)*

TO BARBARA AND LAURA

preface

Engineering education is somewhat of a jig-saw puzzle. Every school ultimately assembles an ECPD accredited engineer, but the order in which he is assembled varies from school to school, and from year to year.

Unlike a jig-saw puzzle, which becomes more difficult to put together as the pieces grow smaller, an engineering curriculum is more easily assembled in small pieces. Indeed, such a program has the additional advantage of both flexibility and mobility. This book, and others in the series which will follow, are intended to furnish small pieces for the educational jig-saw puzzle, insofar as they will cover *topics* rather than *courses*. As such, they are intended to supplement conventional curricula and to implement new ones.

Stagewise Process Design is a complete and self-contained book covering the non-diffusional aspects of material and energy balances under phase equilibrium constraints. McCabe-Thiele and Ponchon methods for handling binary systems as well as *K*-factor and computer methods for multicomponent mixtures are included. The book is intended as an introductory text.

Equipment design procedures are covered in a sufficiently detailed manner to enable students, as well as practicing engineers, to achieve a working knowledge of the principles on which the design of stagewise contactors is based. A knowledge of physical chemistry, thermodynamics, material and energy balances, and calculus is presupposed.

The material covered constitutes a $1\frac{1}{2}$- to $2\frac{1}{2}$-point course in the usual chemical engineering curriculum. For those wishing to use the book as a primary text, problems are included. Institutions using texts resembling condensed versions of the *Chemical Engineers' Handbook* will find that the low price of this book makes it a perfectly reasonable assigned supplementary text.

We express, with gratitude, our thanks to Judy Korman who typed this manuscript. Dr. Erwin Amick, with whom both of us studied stagewise design methods and who contributed many of the end-of-chapter problems, deserves much more than passing thanks. Dr. Eric Bear, Dr. James R. Street, and Dr. Amick provided helpful and critical reviews; and Dr. R. Steinberg contributed many suggestions which considerably strengthened the manuscript.

Hoboken, N.J.
August, 1963

ERNEST J. HENLEY
H. KENNETH STAFFIN

contents

one / *the separation processes*

In a chemical plant, the typically small chemical reactor is virtually hidden among the perplexity of equipment required to purify the raw materials entering the reactor, and the products leaving. This equipment, consisting mostly of stills, filters, crystallizers, extractors and absorbers, generally accomplishes this purification by separating the components of a mixture by virtue of physical property differences.

Very often these differences are properties such as specific gravity or particle size, thus permitting the components of the mixture to be separated mechanically in devices such as a cyclone, centrifuge filter, settler, etc. Design of this type of equipment is dictated primarily by fluid-flow considerations, and will not be considered in this book.

1-1 DIFFUSIONAL OPERATIONS

If the mixture to be separated is a homogeneous, single phase solution, a second phase must generally be formed before a separation of the components in the mixture can be achieved. This second phase can be introduced by adding or removing energy, as in distillation, evaporation, and crystallization, or by introducing an immiscible component as in extraction or gas absorption. In all cases, in order to achieve a separation, we must rely on a predilection on the part of the component to be recovered to collect in one of the immiscible phases, the recovery then being achieved by mechanically separating one phase from the other.

There are two factors which govern the design of equipment wherein components of a mixture are separated by virtue of their

1

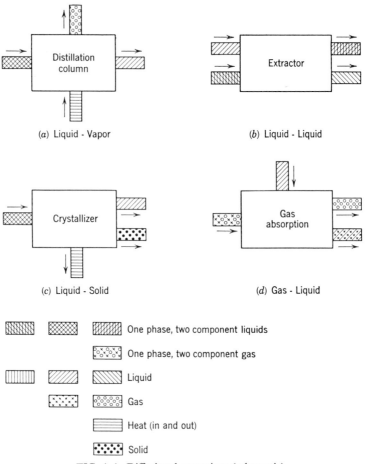

(a) Liquid - Vapor

(b) Liquid - Liquid

(c) Liquid - Solid

(d) Gas - Liquid

One phase, two component liquids

One phase, two component gas

Liquid

Gas

Heat (in and out)

Solid

FIG. 1–1. Diffusional operations (schematic).

being more concentrated in one of the phases: (1) The Thermo-dynamic equilibrium distribution of the components between the phases; (2) The rate of movement, the diffusion, of the component from one phase to the other.

A process in which there is a transfer or separation of chemical species within or between phases by diffusion is called a *diffusional operation*. Figure 1–1 depicts the diffusional operations of dis-tillation, extraction, crystallization, and gas absorption schematically,

TABLE 1-1

Initial Phase	Developed Phase	Operation	How Phase Developed	General Application
Liquid	Vapor	Evaporation	Energy added	Concentration of non-volatile solids in liquid solution
		Distillation	Energy added	Two or more volatile liquids
		Stripping	Inert carrier, gas added	Two or more liquids of different volatility
Liquid	Liquid	Extraction	Immiscible solvent, liquid added	Solutes from solution
Liquid	Solid	Crystallization	Energy removed	Solids from liquids
		Adsorption, ion exchange, hypersorption	Active solid added	Solutes from solution
Gas	Liquid	Absorption	Non-volatile liquid absorbent added	Two or more gases, different solubility
Gas	Solid	Adsorption	Active solid adsorbent added	Two or more gases
Solid	Liquid	Zone melting	Energy added	Metal purification

The Separation Processes / 3

and Table 1–1 defines and lists these and other diffusional operations pertinent to *multiphase* separation processes.

1–2 DIFFUSIONAL SEPARATIONS (SINGLE PHASE)[1]

In some situations it is possible to effect separations of components without creating a new phase. The more common methods of accomplishing this are based on the fact that, in the absence of

TABLE 1–2

APPLICATION OF DIFFUSIONAL OPERATIONS FOR THE
SEPARATION OF THE COMPONENTS IN SINGLE-PHASE
HOMOGENEOUS SOLUTIONS

Initial Phase	Method of Separation	General Application
Liquid	Ultracentrifuge	Large molecule fractionation
Liquid	Electrical	Electroplating
Gaseous	Electromagnetic	Isotope separation of charged species
Gaseous	Thermal Diffusion	Molecules of differing size or shape, or isotopes
Gaseous	Diffusion through inert barriers or membranes	Molecules of differing size or shape, or isotopes

other forces and effects, substances of different molecular weights diffuse at different velocities. Thus mixtures of isotopes, such as $U^{235}F_6$ and $U^{238}F_6$, can be separated by permitting gaseous mixtures of the two components to diffuse through porous media.

Other single-phase separation processes rely on the interjection of a barrier which serves to classify materials according to molecular shape or size (molecular sieving), or on the imposition of external electrical, gravitational, or thermal forces. The details of single

[1] An excellent discussion of single-phase diffusional separations is to be found in Manson Benedict and Thomas Pigford, *Nuclear Chemical Engineering*, McGraw-Hill, New York, 1957.

phase diffusion processes are not discussed in this book. Table 1–2 summarizes the more important of these processes.

1–3 PHYSICAL PROPERTIES AS A CRITERION FOR PROCESS SELECTION

The more common of the diffusional separation processes, and the physical properties on which they are based, are given in Table

TABLE 1–3

PHYSICAL PROPERTIES (IN ADDITION TO DIFFUSIVITY)
ON WHICH SEPARATION PROCESSES ARE BASED

Property	Diffusional Operation Based on the Property
Vapor pressure	Distillation, sublimation, evaporation
Solubility	Crystallization, gas absorption, leaching
Solubility and density	Liquid extraction
Chemical affinity (Van der Waal bonding)	Adsorption, hypersorption, chromatography, foam separation
Adsorption and electrical charge	Ion exchange
Electric charge	Electrodialysis, electrolytic ion exchange
Molecular size and shape	Molecular sieves, membrane permeation
Vapor pressure and velocity	Molecular distillation
Velocity	Gaseous diffusion, thermal diffusion

1–3. Thus the operations of distillation, sublimation, and evaporation all involve the separation of the components of a mixture on the basis of vapor pressure. The term *distillation* is usually applied to liquid mixtures, *evaporation* to the removal of a liquid from a relatively non-volatile liquid or solid, while *sublimation* refers to a process wherein a mixture of solids is separated by vapor pressure differences.

The Separation Processes / 5

Differences in solubility between components make it possible to achieve separations. In *gas absorption*, for instance, a mixture of gases is separated by preferential absorption of one component in a liquid, while *leaching* consists of separating solids by virtue of preferential solubility in liquids. *Liquid extraction* depends on both solubility and density, as is indicated in Fig. 1–1. Here two immiscible liquids of different densities are mixed and one of the components in one of the liquid phases is transferred to the other liquid phase. A difference in density must exist; otherwise, the two immiscible liquid streams could not be separated mechanically. *Molecular distillation* is a process wherein the distillation is carried out at such low pressures that an additional separation takes place because of differences in molecular velocity. *Gaseous diffusion* is a function only of the molecular velocities, whereas in *thermal diffusion* a temperature gradient is superimposed.

Both the absolute magnitude and the magnitude of the differences in physical properties determine whether a given process is technically and economically feasible. If, for instance, we have a solution of compounds having identical boiling points, or solutions which form constant boiling mixtures, isolation of the pure components by ordinary distillation is impossible. In such cases, if distillation is to be used, we must either transform one of the components chemically (such as by esterifying an acid to reduce its boiling point), or we may add a third component which will alter the vapor pressure characteristics of the system. Another example of a situation where distillation cannot be used is when one of the components is heat labile or has an intolerably high boiling point. At very high boiling temperatures, the problem of designing heat transfer facilities at practical heat transfer rates assumes major proportions and the investment costs become rather high.

1–4   FACTORS IN PROCESS SELECTION

Provided the physical properties are such that more than one separation process can be used to achieve product specifications, the choice of process is dictated by cost considerations. The requirements of product specification, however, often govern the selection of the process. For example, if it is necessary to produce a metal having less than a few parts per million of impurities, we may turn to zone melting even though vacuum distillation may be cheaper. Similarly, if the sales requirements of a process are such that the product must be in the form of a free-flowing, white granular powder, the process must be geared to meet these specifications.

The cost factors to be considered in a process design include:

1. *Engineering Design and Development.* If the operation chosen is an established one, equipment based on a standard mechanical design can be purchased. The differences in cost between using a conventional process with standard facilities and developing and testing special-purpose designs are usually very great.

2. *Fixed Investment.* Fixed investment includes equipment and installation costs. Variations in fabrication costs are a function of geometric complexity and materials of construction. An extraction which can be carried out at room temperature may be more economical than a corrosive high-temperature distillation, on a material of construction basis alone.

3. *Operating Expenses.* In addition to the usual costs incurred in keeping any piece of machinery in operation, there are unique problems in the chemical industry, the chief of these being loss of product and reagents. In the average chemical plant, a $100,000 piece of equipment processes perhaps $10,000,000 worth of material every year. Thus a one per cent difference in operating efficiency can be used to justify replacement of the entire unit.

4. *Operability.* Although there are no clear-cut criteria for what is an operable or non-operable design, the operating experience and judgement of the plant engineers must be taken into account. There is an understandable resistance to unusual mechanical designs, high-speed rotating machinery, fragile materials of construction and generally hard to maintain equipment.

1-5 THE IDEAL STAGE CONCEPT

A concept of importance in the development of the relationships used in the design of contact equipment is that of the *equilibrium stage*. In an operation such as the one shown schematically in Fig. 1-2, A_{out} and B_{out} are in thermodynamic equilibrium; hence, their compositions are dictated by equilibrium constraints (the solubility or vapor pressure relationships, for instance).

When two or more phases are brought into contact with each other in a closed system, and sufficient residence time is allowed, the components of the composite mixture will distribute themselves

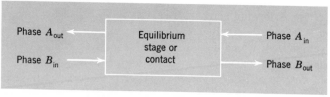

FIG. 1-2. An equilibrium stage.

between the phases in a manner determined only by the thermo-dynamic equilibrium for that system. Upon separation of phases of the equilibrium mixture, the initial materials are said to have been subjected to a single equilibrium in an *equilibrium stage* or *contact*. If the equilibrium relations for the system are known, the compositions and amounts of each phase leaving the stage can be accurately determined. By utilizing equilibrium data and making the appropriate material balances we can calculate the number of *theoretical stages* required to effect a given separation.

1-6 MULTIPLE STAGE ARRANGEMENT

Three basic flow arrangements between stages are possible. In Fig. 1-3 the phases A and B in (a) are in co-current, or parallel, flow between stages 1 and 2. The concept of cross flow is illustrated in

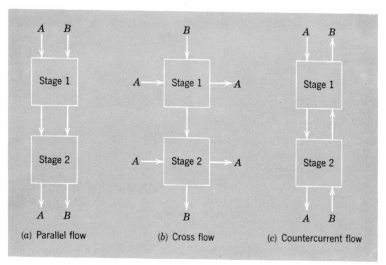

FIG. 1-3. Stage arrangements.

(b), phase A flowing across the stages, while phase B moves from stage 1 to stage 2. Truly countercurrent operation is shown in (c).

Example 1–1, which demonstrates the basic concepts involved in making material balances about equilibrium stages, also illustrates how the material balances become a function of the stage arrangement.

EXAMPLE 1–1. Uranium in the form of uranyl nitrate (UN) dissolved in water is to be recovered from an aqueous solution. The first step in the recovery is a liquid-liquid extraction, the UN being extracted from the water with tributyl phosphate (TBP). Water and TBP are mutually insoluble, and the mass distribution coefficient of UN between water and TBP is 5.5, independent of composition.

$$\frac{\text{Pounds UN}}{\text{Pounds TBP}} = 5.5 \frac{\text{Pounds UN}}{\text{Pounds } H_2O}$$

A 10% (wt) solution of UN in H_2O is to be treated with 150 lb of TBP. Ninety-eight percent of the UN in the water is to be extracted in a series of equilibrium stages. How many stages are required in (a) countercurrent flow, (b) parallel flow, (c) cross-flow, the TBP phase in equal portions flowing across the H_2O phase which is passing along the stages [see Fig. 1–4(c)].

Solution: Basis: 100 lb of H_2O containing 10% UN.

(a) Assuming there is only one stage, Fig. 1–4(a) let $y =$ lb UN in the TBP phase leaving the stage, and let $x =$ lb UN in the water phase leaving. The streams (x lb UN, 90 lb H_2O) and (y lb UN, 150 lb TBP) are in equilibrium, the equilibrium relationship being:

$$\frac{x}{90}(5.5) = \frac{y}{150} \tag{1-1}$$

Furthermore, taking an overall UN material balance about the stage,

$$x + y = 10 \tag{1-2}$$

Solving Eqs. 1–1 and 1–2 simultaneously,

$$x = 0.985 \qquad y = 9.015$$

$$\text{UN recovered} = 90.15\%$$

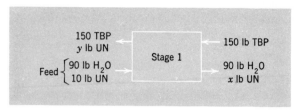

FIG. 1–4(a). Flow sheet for Example 1–1.

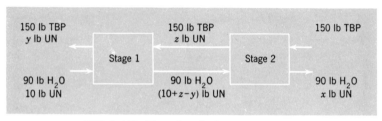

FIG. 1–4(b). Flow sheet for Example 1–1.

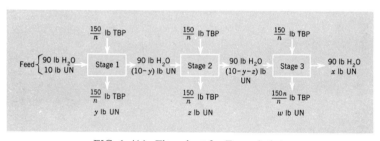

FIG. 1–4(c). Flow sheet for Example 1–1.

This is inadequate. We will try two stages, Fig. 1–4(b). There is an equilibrium relationship for each stage:

Stage 1	Stage 2
Equilibrium Relationship:	Equilibrium Relationship:

$$\frac{(10 + z - y)}{90}(5.5) = \frac{y}{150} \qquad \frac{x}{90}(5.5) = \frac{z}{150}$$

Solving simultaneously with the overall UN balance,

$$y = 9.89, \qquad x = 0.11, \qquad \text{Recovery} = 98.9\%$$

(*b*) Parallel flow ((*a*) in Fig. 1–3) gives the equivalent of one equilibrium stage, no matter how many tanks are placed in series. Parallel flow is used only if there is a physical restriction on the geometric size of a single stage.

(*c*) The flow sheet for cross flow is given in Fig. 1–4(*c*) for $n = 3$ stages. The percentage of recovery as a function of the number of stages is:

$n = 1$; UN recovery: 90.15% [same as (*a*) and (*b*)]
$n = 2$; UN recovery: 96.8% [lower than (*a*), higher than (*b*)]
$n = 3$; UN recovery: 98.7%

Pure cross-flow operations are used only if one of the phases is very difficult to pump. Then only one stage with successive extractant streams would normally be employed.

The ratio $\left(\dfrac{\text{Parts UN}}{\text{Parts TBP}}\right) \Big/ \left(\dfrac{\text{Parts UN}}{\text{Parts H}_2\text{O}}\right)$ of Example 1–1 is called a distribution coefficient in extraction, but more generally the separation factor, α_{AB}

$$\alpha_{AB} = \frac{\left(\dfrac{\text{Conc of }A}{\text{Conc of }B}\right)\text{Phase 1}}{\left(\dfrac{\text{Conc of }A}{\text{Conc of }B}\right)\text{Phase 2}}$$

It will be shown in Chapter 4 that for nearly all systems, the number of stages required to achieve a given separation varies inversely with the log of α.

1–7 RATE OF APPROACH TO EQUILIBRIUM

The rate at which the system approaches the ultimate equilibrium condition, in general, cannot be predicted analytically. For diffusional rate processes which are diffusion controlled, the speed of approach to the equilibrium condition is directly proportional to the concentration driving force and inversely proportional to the resistance to mass transfer of the components from one phase to another. It follows, therefore, that the rate of approach to equilibrium of a system will depend not only on the departure of the system from the thermodynamic equilibrium, but also on the many mechanical factors of stage design which establish turbulence and intimacy of contact, thereby controlling the rate of mass transfer.

Since the rate at which a system approaches an equilibrium condition depends on the concentration differences, the rate becomes progressively slower as equilibrium is approached, and in the strictest sense an infinite time would be required to achieve the ultimate condition. Actually, with suitable agitation in a closed stage, compositions corresponding within experimental error to those calculated from the system thermodynamics can be readily achieved. In an actual separation process, however, it is often not feasible to employ the closed-stage method of contact. For operations in which a large volume of gas is brought into contact with a liquid or solid, single closed-stage contact is almost impossible. It is far easier to employ a continuous type of phase contacting device.

If, instead of operating with a closed system, we provide for continuous feed and withdrawal of each of the phases to the stage, it is extremely unlikely that exit streams will approach equilibrium. This is particularly true at high flow rates where a relatively short time is allowed for phase contact, and the possibility of the phases by-passing each other without achieving good contact is great. Such, in fact, is the condition that occurs in practice with all contact stages operating under flow conditions. One measure of the efficiency of an actual stage operating with flowing phases is the degree to which the exit stream compositions approach the value possible in a hypothetical equilibrium stage. (The concept of stage efficiency is discussed in Chapter 4.)

two / *thermodynamic equilibrium diagrams*

Stagewise calculations involve the simultaneous solution of material and energy balances with the equilibrium relationships. In Example 1-1 a computation of this sort could be done analytically very quickly because (1) only a few stages were required, (2) no energy balance was needed, the entire process being assumed isothermal, and (3) the equilibrium relationship was a simple one. In cases involving many stages, complex equilibrium functions, and energy balances, the number of simultaneous equations involved in the solution of the problem becomes sufficiently great to make analytical solutions by manual means impractically complex. In these situations, an analytical solution is facilitated by means of electronic computers. Frequently, when problems of these types involve only two or three components, graphical techniques provide a convenient solution approach without resort to a machine computer. These graphical methods involve establishing the simultaneous solution by plotting material balance lines on thermodynamic equilibrium diagrams. Some of the more commonly used thermodynamic equilibrium diagrams useful in stagewise calculation problems will be developed in this chapter.

2-1 THE PHASE RULE
The mathematical basis for examining phase equilibrium diagrams is Gibbs' phase rule,[1]

---

[1] It is recommended that the reader refer to a physical chemistry or thermodynamics textbook for a detailed discussion of the phase rule.

$$F = C - P + 2$$

where F = Degrees of freedom
  P = Phases
  C = Components

The terms can be understood by considering the three points, A, B, C, on the one-component two-variable (P-T) phase diagram, Fig. 2-1. At A, we have $C = 1$, $P = 1$ and F, the degrees of freedom, $= 2$.

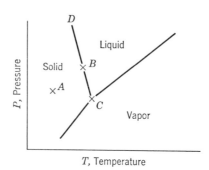

FIG. 2-1. Pressure-temperature phase equilibrium diagram.

Hence, we can change any two of the thermodynamic variables, pressure and temperature, and not introduce any new phases. At B we have one degree of freedom; an increase in pressure, for instance, will not necessarily result in the solid (in the mixture of solid and liquid) being liquefied, because we can always lower the temperature and remain on the phase envelope $\overline{DC}$. At C there are no degrees of freedom and a change of pressure or temperature results in the disappearance of a phase, no matter what value the other variable assumes. These considerations apply to all diagrams whether the variables be intensive or extensive (independent or dependent on total mass).

2-2 TWO COMPONENT SYSTEMS, DISTILLATION

Here we have a two-component, A and B, system with two phases, gas and liquid, and four independent variables; P, T, and the concentrations of one of the components (A) in the gas and liquid, y_A and x_A. The concentrations of B, y_B and x_B are not independent variables; so for convenience the subscript A will henceforth be dropped. By the phase rule we have two degrees of freedom.

Let us now examine the various types of isobaric (constant pressure) phase diagrams we can draw. Of the four possible diagrams T-x-y, x-y, T-x, T-y, only the T-x-y and x-y diagrams are widely used, the x-y diagrams being known as a McCabe-Thiele plot. The T-x-y and x-y diagrams are shown in Fig. 2–2.

In (a) of Fig. 2–2, for a two-phase system if we specify x, since P is given and $F = 2 - 2 + 2 = 2$, the system is invariant and y and T, the two other variables, are uniquely fixed. Translating this concept to (b) in Fig. 2–2, we see that every point on the isobaric equilibrium

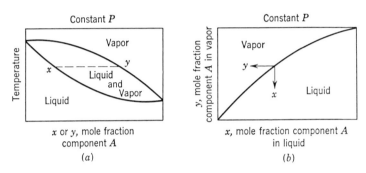

FIG. 2–2. Vapor-liquid phase equilibrium.

line is at a different saturation temperature, if the pressure is constant. Alternatively, (b) in Fig. 2–2 might have been constructed for a constant-temperature, variable-pressure situation. The construction and use of T-x-y and x-y diagrams are discussed in Example 2–1.

Other diagrams, namely, the series at constant x or y, could be constructed; however, these are used only rarely in design calculations. If there are three components (A, B, C) instead of two, there will be six variables (T, P, x_A, x_B, y_A, y_B) instead of the four in a binary system. It is inconvenient to represent this many variables in a two dimensional plot.

EXAMPLE 2–1. Vapor pressures for n-hexane, H, and n-octane, O, are given in Table 2–1. Assuming that Raoult's and Dalton's laws apply, construct T-x-y and x-y plots for this system at one atmosphere.

(a) When a solution containing 30 mole percent H is vaporized, what is the composition of the initial vapor formed?

(b) If this vapor is condensed to a saturated liquid and a differential amount of vapor is formed from this condensate, what would be its composition? Show the processes (a) and (b) on the x-y and T-x-y diagrams.

(c) If a 20% H solution were boiled until 60% of the liquid phase has been vaporized, what will be the composition of the vapor and liquid formed?

TABLE 2–1

VAPOR PRESSURES IN mm Hg FOR
HEXANE-OCTANE
(From Perry, *Chemical Engineers' Handbook*, McGraw-Hill, 3rd ed., 1950)

Temp, °F	Hexane	Octane
155.7	760	121
175	1025	173
200	1480	278
225	2130	434
250	3000	654
258.2	3420	760

Solution: *Basis:*   One mole of liquid.

According to Raoult's law,

$$p_H = P_H^\circ x_H \quad \text{and} \quad p_O = P_O^\circ x_O \quad (2\text{--}1)$$

where P_O° and P_H° = vapor pressure of octane and hexane
      p_O and p_H = partial pressure of octane and hexane in vapor

By Dalton's law,

$$p_H = P y_H \quad \text{and} \quad p_O = P y_O \quad (2\text{--}2)$$

where P = total pressure. Also,

$$p_H + p_O = P, \quad x_H + x_O = 1, \quad \text{and} \quad y_H + y_O = 1$$

Eliminating p_H between Eqs. 2–2 and 2–1,

$$y_H = \left(\frac{P_H^\circ}{P} \right) x_H \quad (2\text{--}3)$$

Consecutive substitution of $y_H = (1 - y_O)$, Eq. 2–2, Eq. 2–1, and $x_O = (1 - x_H)$ into Eq. 2–3 gives

$$\frac{P - P_O^\circ}{P_H^\circ - P_O^\circ} = x_H \qquad (2\text{–}4)$$

We now assume a temperature and calculate x_H from Eq. 2–4 and y_H from Eq. 2–3. At 175°F, for instance,

$$x_H = \frac{760 - 173}{1025 - 173} = 0.69; \qquad y_H = \frac{1025}{760}(0.69) = 0.93$$

The results of the calculations are shown in Figs. 2–3 and 2–4 (heavy lines). The line $y = x$, on Fig. 2–3, is also shown. It is a useful reference line because in condensing a vapor we move horizontally from the vapor-liquid equilibrium line to the $y = x$ line, since the newly formed liquid must have the same composition as the (now condensed) vapor.

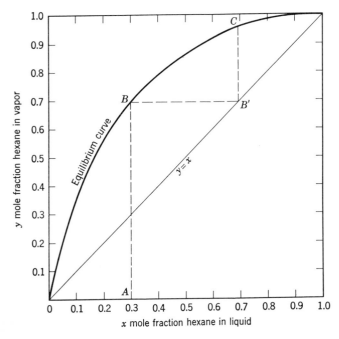

FIG. 2–3. x-y Diagram for hexane-octane.

(a) The vaporization is shown by line A-B in Fig. 2–3, and line A_0-A in Fig. 2–4. The paths A-B and A_0-A represent isobaric heating of the liquid, $x = 0.3$. From Fig. 2–4 we see that boiling takes place at 210°F, the vapor formed, B, having the composition of $y = 0.7$. Although Fig. 2–3 does not show temperatures, it does tell us that a saturated liquid of $x = 0.3$ is in equilibrium with a saturated vapor of $y = 0.7$ at point B.

(b) The vapor at B is totally condensed, B-B', and revaporized, B'-C. At C, the concentration of hexane in the vapor is 0.93. Note that it is necessary to assume that only a differential amount of vapor be formed; otherwise, the composition of the liquid will change (as in part c which follows).

(c) This process can be shown directly on Fig. 2–4. We move along the path G-E until by trial and error we locate the isotherm $\overline{DEF}$ such that it divides the $x = 0.2$ line into segments so that the ratio of liquid to vapor, $L/V = 0.4/0.6 = \overline{FE}/\overline{ED}$, $x = 0.08$, and

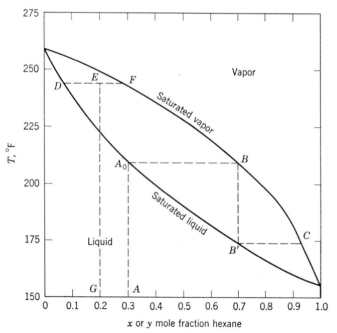

FIG. 2-4. *T-x-y* Diagram for hexane-octane.

$y = 0.29.$[1] This solution can also be accomplished by trial and error, since a hexane balance yields

$$yV + xL = (1)(0.2)$$
$$(y)(0.6) + (x)(0.4) = 0.2$$

and the points y and x must lie on the equilibrium curve.

2–3 NON-IDEAL SYSTEMS

There are variations in both the type and degree of non-ideality. In Example 2–1, for instance, we calculated x-y data from vapor pressure data, assuming that the system followed Raoult's and Dalton's laws. A still more stringent assumption, namely, that the liquid phase is an ideal solution and the gas an ideal gas, leads to the approximation (see Eq. 2–3):

$$y_H = \frac{P_H^\circ}{P} x_H = K_H x_H \qquad (2\text{–}5)$$

where $K_H = K$ factor for hexane.

If both K_H and K_O, the K factor for octane, are assumed constant and independent of temperature, this defines the relative volatility, α.

$$\alpha = \frac{K_H}{K_O} = \frac{P_H^\circ}{P_O^\circ} = \frac{y_H/x_H}{y_O/x_O} = \frac{y_H/x_H}{(1 - y_H)/(1 - x_H)} \qquad (2\text{–}6)$$

Rearranging Eq. 2–6,

$$y/x = y + \alpha(1 - y)$$

[1] This is an application of the well known "lever rule." Let M_E, M_D, and M_F be the masses of total mixture, liquid, and vapor, respectively, and z_E, x_D and y_F the corresponding mole fractions of H. A material balance for H gives:

$$M_E z_E = (M_D + M_F)z_E = M_D x_D + M_F y_F$$

Solving for the ratio of liquid to vapor,

$$\frac{M_D}{M_F} = \frac{L}{V} = \frac{y_F - z_E}{z_E - x_D} = \frac{\overline{FE}}{\overline{ED}}$$

Likewise,

$$\frac{M_D}{M_E} = \frac{L}{L + V} = \frac{y_F - z_E}{y_F - x_D} = \frac{\overline{FE}}{\overline{FD}}$$

and

$$\frac{M_F}{M_E} = \frac{V}{L + V} = \frac{z_E - x_D}{y_F - x_D} = \frac{\overline{ED}}{\overline{FD}}$$

Inspection of the vapor pressure data for the H-O system, Table 2-1, reveals that α for this system varies from $\alpha = 760/121 = 6.3$ at 155.7°F to $3420/760 = 4.51$ at 258.2°F.

Thus, if the x-y data had been calculated from Eq. 2–6, assuming a constant α obtained from a single isothermal K value, errors would be incurred.

The assumption of constant α, or of Raoult's law, results in catastrophic errors if the system of interest forms a *constant boiling mixture*, or *azeotrope*.

2–4 THREE-COMPONENT SYSTEM, EXTRACTION

To extract a desired component A from a homogeneous liquid solution we generally introduce another liquid phase which is insoluble with the one containing A. In a practical situation A is present in low concentrations, and we have a system consisting of two mutually insoluble carrier solutions between which the *solute A* is distributed. The solution rich in A is called the *extract* phase, E (usually the solvent layer); the treated solution, poor in A, is called the *raffinate*, R.

In the usual case there will be some mutual solubility between the two solvents. If we designate one solvent as B and the other as S, the thermodynamic variables for the system are T, P, x_{AE}, x_{BE}, x_{AR}, x_{BR}, the concentration of S not being a variable at any given T and P, since $x_{AE} + x_{BE} + x_{SE} = 1$ and $x_{AR} + x_{BR} + x_{SR} = 1$. According to the phase rule, there are three degrees of freedom ($F = 3 - 2 + 2$). Hence, if at constant T and P, any one variable, say x_{AE}, is designated, all other variables (x_{BE}, x_{AR}, and x_{BR}) are fixed.

This is demonstrated in (a) and (b) of Fig. 2–5, both of which are schematic equilibrium diagrams for three component equilibrium mixtures. In (a) of Fig. 2–5 the data are plotted on a triangular diagram where the three apexes represent pure A, B, and S. The two-phase region is enclosed within the saturation line, the region to the right of the "plait point" denoting saturated solvent rich (extract) phase, the region to the left being the saturated raffinate phase. At the plait point the two phases have identical compositions. According to the phase rule, at a fixed T, P, and x_{AE}, the compositions x_{BE}, x_{SE}, x_{AR}, x_{BR}, and x_{SR} are also fixed. This is shown by the tie line $\overline{FG}$ which connects the point x_{AE} (the concentration of A in the extract phase) with x_{AR} (the concentration of A in the

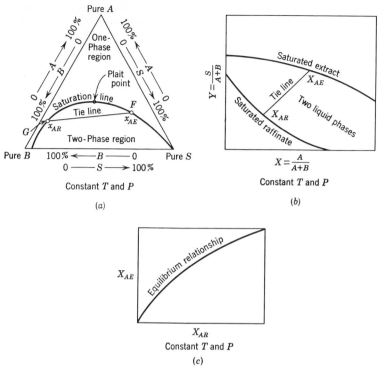

FIG. 2–5. Three-component phase equilibrium diagram.

raffinate phase) in equilibrium with x_{AE}. The location of the tie lines as well as the equilibrium phase envelope must be determined experimentally.

This same information is translated to (b) of Fig. 2–5, another type of diagram used for this purpose. Here the coordinates are on a solvent-free basis; thus the slope of a line such as $\overline{X_{AR}X_{AE}}$ is S/A, the ratio of solvent to solute.[1] Diagrams of this type were first proposed by Janecke.[2]

If the two solvents, B and S, are completely insoluble, then the situation is simplified because there are then only four variables, T, P, x_{AE}, and x_{AR}, and we can conveniently construct a plot of the

[1] x and y are used to denote mole or mass fractions. X and Y signify mass or mole ratios.

[2] Janecke, E., *Z. Anorg. Chemie*, **51**, 132 (1906).

type shown in (c) of Fig. 2–5. Note that this diagram is directly analogous to Fig. 2–3, with the exception of the temperature constraint. The type of diagram shown in (c) of Fig. 2–5 could, of course, be drawn if there were mutual solubility between the phases; however, in that case it is not conveniently used for material balance calculations, as will be seen in Examples 2–2 and 2–3.

EXAMPLE 2–2. Furfural (F) is suggested as a solvent for removing ethylene glycol (G) from water (W). The equilibrium solubility and tie line data at 25°C are given in Tables 2–2 and 2–3. Using these

TABLE 2–2

EQUILIBRIUM DATA IN WEIGHT PERCENT:
FURFURAL, GLYCOL, WATER

Furfural %	Glycol %	Water %
94.8	0.0	5.2
84.4	11.4	4.1
63.1	29.7	7.2
49.4	41.6	9.0
40.6	47.5	11.9
33.8	50.1	16.1
23.2	52.9	23.9
20.1	50.6	29.4
10.2	32.2	57.6
9.2	28.1	62.2
7.9	0.0	92.1

TABLE 2–3

MUTUAL EQUILIBRIUM (TIE-LINE) DATA FOR FURFURAL-
ETHYLENE GLYCOL-WATER

Glycol in Water Layer, %	Glycol in Solvent Layer, %
7.7	28.9
6.1	21.9
4.8	14.3
2.3	7.3
11.5	41.8
32.1	48.8

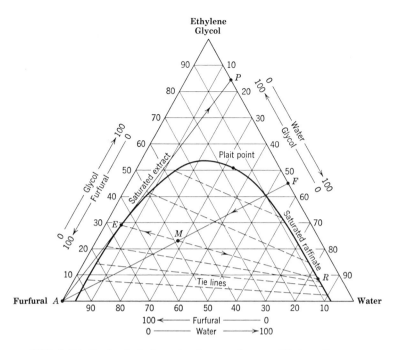

FIG. 2–6A. Furfural-ethylene glycol-water phase equilibrium diagram.

data, construct the type of phase equilibrium diagrams shown in Fig. 2–5.

(a) Calculate the composition of the equilibrium phases produced when a 45% by weight glycol-in-water solution is contacted with its own weight of furfural. Show the process on each of the diagrams.

(b) Using Fig. 2–6A only, show the composition of the water-glycol mixture obtained if all the furfural is removed from the extract obtained in (a).

Solution: Basis: 100 lb of 45% glycol-in-water solution.

(a) In Fig. 2–6A the point F marks the composition 0% furfural, 45% glycol, 55% water. As we add furfural to this mixture we follow the path $F \rightarrow A$. When we reach the point M, where $\overline{AM}/\overline{FM} = 1/1$, we have obtained a mixture which is half furfural and half feed (F). Since the resulting mixture M is in the two phase region, it separates into two phases, the extract phase, E (28.5% G,

6.5% W, 65.0% F), and raffinate, R (8% G, 84% W, 8% F), given by the equilibrium tie line through M.

We can now solve for the amount of raffinate and extract phases.

$$\text{Overall balance:} \quad R + E = 200 \text{ lb}$$
$$\text{Furfural balance:} \quad 0.65E + 0.08R = 100 \text{ lb}$$

Solving:

$$R = 52.6 \text{ lb} \quad \text{and} \quad E = 147.4 \text{ lb}$$

This answer could also have been obtained from the length of the tie lines, $E = 200\ (\overline{RM}/\overline{RE})$ and $R = 200\ (\overline{EM}/\overline{ER})$.

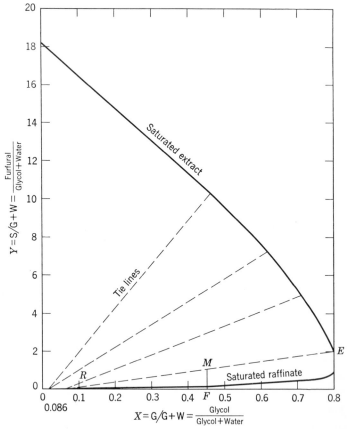

FIG. 2–6B. Furfural-ethylene glycol-water phase equilibrium diagram.

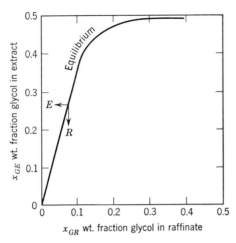

FIG. 2–6C. Furfural-ethylene glycol-water phase equilibrium diagram.

The same process can be followed on Fig. 2–6B. Here, starting at $F = 0.45$, we follow a vertical path (addition of pure solvent) to point M, where $S/(G + W) = 1$. This mixture then separates into the E and R, extract and raffinate streams shown.

Figure 2–6C is relatively useless for doing a graphical solution. The point E-R can, however, be found by a trial and error calculation, since

$$E + R = 200$$
$$x_{GE}E + x_{GR}R = (100)(0.45)$$

The x_{GE} and x_{GR} which satisfy these equations are obtained by trial and error from Fig. 2–6C.

(b) The path followed is E to P in Fig. 2–6A; the extract composition is 82.5% glycol, 17.5% water.

2–5 THREE-COMPONENT SYSTEM, ABSORPTION

If a liquid is used to selectively absorb one of the components from a gas stream, the process is analogous to extraction. If for example, a liquid S is used to separate gas B from A, the thermodynamic variables are P, T, x_A, x_B, y_A, y_B. Again there are three degrees of freedom; hence, if three variables, P, T, and y_A, are specified, all other variables are determined and phase equilibrium diagrams such as (a) and (b) in Fig. 2–7 can be constructed, (a) being

Thermodynamic Equilibrium Diagrams | 25

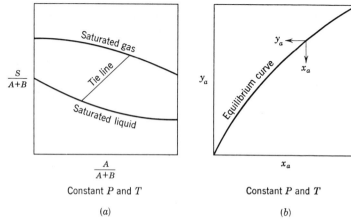

FIG. 2–7. Gas-liquid phase equilibrium diagram.

analogous to (b) in Fig. 2–5, and (b) being analogous to (c) in Fig. 2–5. Should the solvent S have negligible vapor pressure, and if the carrier gas is insoluble in S, then the only variables remaining are P, T, x_A, y_A.

Gas absorption is characterized by the presence of a negligible amount of the liquid solvent in the vapor phase, hence diagrams such as (a) in Fig. 2–7 are rarely used.

EXAMPLE 2–3. The partial pressure of ammonia in air-ammonia mixtures in equilibrium with its aqueous solution at 20°C is given in Table 2–4. Using these data, and neglecting the vapor pressure of

TABLE 2–4

PARTIAL PRESSURE OF AMMONIA OVER AMMONIA-
WATER SOLUTIONS AT 20°C
Data from Perry, op. cit., p. 171)

NH$_3$ Partial Pressure, Hg	gNH$_3$/gH$_2$O
31.7	0.05
69.6	0.10
114	0.15
166	0.20
227	0.25

water and the solubility of air in water, construct an equilibrium diagram analogous to (b) in Fig. 2–7, using mole ratios Y_A = moles NH_3/mole air, X_A = moles NH_3/mole H_2O as coordinates.

(a) If 10 moles of gas, of composition $Y = 0.3$, are contacted with 10 moles of a solution of composition $X = 0.1$, what will be the composition of the resulting phases at equilibrium? The process is isothermal.

Solution: Basis: 10 moles of gas, $Y = 0.3$, and 10 moles of liquid, $X = 0.1$.

The equilibrium data given in Table 2–4 were recalculated (Table 2–5) and plotted (Fig. 2–8).

The mixing process is shown in the insert in Fig. 2–8. Immediately upon contact, the mixture is at point F. The ratio of Y/X = moles H_2O/mole air = 9.09/7.7 = 1.19; hence a line through F of slope 1.19 marks the locus of all possible mixtures of the two phases. The slope is negative because in the transfer ΔY is negative, and ΔX is positive. At equilibrium the composition of the mixture leaving the stage is at point A on the equilibrium curve. Hence

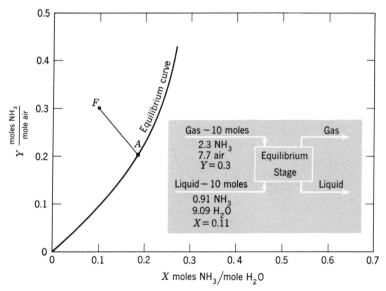

FIG. 2–8. Equilibrium data for air-NH_3-H_2O.

TABLE 2–5

Y-X DATA FOR AMMONIA-WATER, 20°C

Y Moles NH_3/Mole Air	X Moles NH_3/Mole H_2O
0.044	0.053
0.101	0.100
0.176	0.159
0.311	0.212
0.425	0.265

$Y = 0.195$, $X = 0.19$. This result can be checked by a NH_3 balance, since the amount of NH_3 leaving is $(0.195)(7.70) + 0.19(9.09) = 3.21$, which equals the amount of NH_3 entering.

2–6 VARIABLES OTHER THAN CONCENTRATION

The phase equilibrium diagrams shown have been in terms of T, P, and concentrations. Actually, any thermodynamic function can be used in place of T, P, or concentration. In distillation, for instance, it is sometimes convenient to work in terms of enthalpy, because the diagram can then be used to show heat addition or removal as well as composition changes. It is interesting to note that, since the enthalpies of the vapor and liquid are different, the total enthalpy depends on the amounts of the phases as well as their compositions. This is best demonstrated by Fig. 2–9 which is a composition-enthalpy diagram at constant pressure. The similarity in shape between Figs. 2–5(b), 2–7(a), and 2–9 is more than coincidental. An example demonstrating the construction and utility of an enthalpy-composition (Ponchon-Savarit)[1] diagram follows.

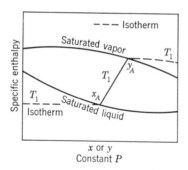

FIG. 2–9. Composition-enthalpy phase equilibrium diagram.

[1] Ponchon, M., *Tech. Moderne*, **13**, 20, 53 (1921) and Savarit, R., *Arts et Metiers*, **65**, 142, 178, 241, 266, 307 (1922).

EXAMPLE 2–4. Using the thermodynamic data in Table 2–6 and the vapor-liquid equilibrium data from Example 2–1, construct an enthalpy composition diagram (H-x-y) for the system hexane-octane. Use a thermodynamic base of enthalpy = 0 at 0°C for the

TABLE 2–6

THERMODYNAMIC DATA, HEXANE-OCTANE

(Rossini, F., "Selected Values of Thermodynamic Constant for Hydrocarbons," A. P. I. Project 44, 1958)

Octane

H_v = 8215 cal/g mole at 125.8°C (boiling point)

C_p (gas) = $10.63 + 0.1361T - 42.59(10^6)T^2$ cal/g mole ($T = °K$)

C_p (liquid) = 61.5 cal/g mole °C

Hexane

H_v = 6900 cal/g mole at 68.5°C (boiling point)

C_p (gas) = $7.48 + 0.1044T - 32.47(10^6)T^2$ cal/g mole ($T = °K$)

C_p (liquid) = 45.1 cal/g mole °C

saturated liquid, and assume the latent heats are independent of temperature and composition.

(a) Solve parts (a) and (c) of Example 2–1, assuming in each case that the liquid is initially at 70°C. Calculate the amount of heat added in each case, per g mole.

Construction of H-x-y diagram, Fig. 2–10:

The end points of the saturated liquid and vapor envelopes are located as follows:

$$\text{Hexane (sat'd liquid)} = \int_0^{68.5} C_p \, dT = (68.5)(45.1)$$
$$= 3,100 \text{ cal/g mole}$$

$$\text{Hexane (sat'd vapor)} = 3,100 + H_v = 3,100 + 6,900$$
$$= 10,000 \text{ cal/g mole}$$

$$\text{Octane (sat'd liquid)} = \int_0^{125.8} C_p \, dT = (125.8)(61.5)$$
$$= 7,7000 \text{ cal/g mole}$$

$$\text{Octane (sat'd vapor)} = 7,700 + H_v = 7,700 + 8,215$$
$$= 15,915 \text{ cal/g mole}$$

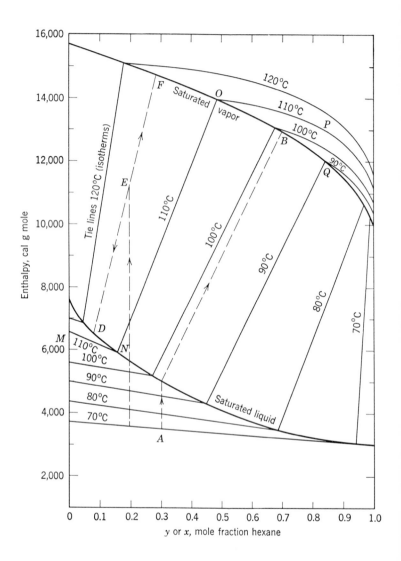

FIG. 2–10. *H-x-y* Diagram for hexane-octane.

The isotherms can now be located. Consider the one at 110°C. At 110°C and $x = 0$,

$$H = \int_0^{110} C_p\, dT = (110)(61.5) = 6{,}750 \text{ cal/g mole (point } M\text{)}$$

From Fig. 2–4, the composition which boils at 110°C is $x = 0.16$ and the vapor is equilibrium with $x = 0.16$ is $y = 0.49$.

The enthalpy of saturated liquid of $x = 0.16$ (point N) is

$$\int_0^{110} (0.16)(110)(61.5) + \int_0^{110} (0.84)(110)(45.1) = 6055 \text{ cal/g mole}$$

The enthalpy of the saturated vapor (point O) is

$$6055 + (0.49)(6{,}900) + (0.51)(8{,}215) = 14{,}000 \text{ cal/g mole}$$

Points in the superheated vapor region were obtained by first integrating the C_p expression to get enthalpy data. This was done, and the results are shown in Fig. 2–11. To obtain the enthalpy of a typical point, $y = 0.84$ vapor at 110°C, we calculate the amount of superheat above the saturated vapor temperature $(\overline{PQ})$, which for $y = 0.84$ is 90°C.

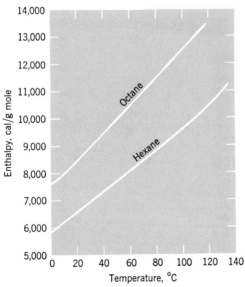

FIG. 2–11. Enthalpies of hexane and octane.

At 110°C, H octane = 13,300 cal/g mole
At 90°C, H octane = 12,000 cal/g mole

Difference   1,300 cal/g mole

At 110°C, H hexane = 10,100 cal/g mole
At 90°C, H hexane = 9,200 cal/g mole

Difference   900 cal/g mole

At 90°C, enthalpy of saturated vapor mixture from Fig. 2–10 = 12,100 cal/g mole (point Q).

Therefore,   12,500 + (0.84)(900) + (0.16)(1,300) = 13,060   cal/g mole is the enthalpy of the y = 0.84 mixture at 110°C (point P).

(a) The path A to B denotes the path of vaporization; y = 0.7. The heat added is 13,400 − 3,500 = 9,900 cal/g mole.

(c) The vertical line at x = 0.2 is extended until it cuts an isotherm such that $\overline{DE}/\overline{EF}$ = 6/4. The temperature is 117°C, y = 0.29, x = 0.08. The heat added is 11,000 − 3,600 = 7,400 cal/g mole.

2–7 "UNUSUAL TECHNIQUES"

Distillation, absorption, and extraction, in that order, are the most common of the separation processes. Techniques for designing and building equipment of this type are essentially in the cook-book state. When a new separation method such as ion exchange, hypersorption, or zone melting is developed, new design procedures must be used.

The cornerstone of chemical engineering rests on the so-called Unit Operations concept, namely, that the design methods used to build distillation columns, for instance, are the same irrespective of what is being distilled. There will be mechanical differences in columns built to separate fatty acids and those in which liquid oxygen is produced, but the similarities greatly overshadow the differences. Furthermore, the classical design methods are generalized to such an extent that there are marked similarities in the way distillation, absorption, and extraction columns are designed.

Hence, when design methods for a new separation technique are to be developed, they are formalized in such a fashion that we can readily use the "standard" McCabe-Thiele or Ponchon-Savarit diagrams and concepts. In this fashion, a systematic and orderly body of knowledge has been developed.

Baytown Refinery, Humble Oil and Refining Co. Light ends fractionating unit.
Left to right:

Column	Trays	Bubble caps	Capacity B/SD	Material of construction
1. Debutanizer	30	6″ circular	18,000	Quality steel
2. Depropanizer	45	4½″ circular	21,000	Quality steel
3. Pentane splitter	50	Type B	12,000	Quality steel
4. C$_4$ splitter	50	6″ circular	. . .	Quality steel
5. Debutanizer	45	4″ circular	18,340	Quality steel
6. Alkylation rerun	18	. . .	. . .	Quality steel

Photo courtesy of Standard Oil Co. (N.J.).

three / equipment for stagewise contacts

This chapter deals with the general problems a process designer faces in selecting equipment. The more quantitative aspects are considered in Chapter 10.

3-1 FACTORS IN EQUIPMENT DESIGN

In all commonly used physical separations, two phases must be contacted and then separated. The exact manner by which the contact and separations are accomplished depends on the type of operation and the nature of the mixture.

In Fig. 3-1 we see four equilibrium stages or contacts with a "light" phase, A, moving countercurrent to a "heavy" phase, B. The light and heavy phases may be gas and liquid, as in distillation or gas absorption, or two immiscible liquids, as in extraction. If each contact were a perfect equilibrium stage, streams B_1 and A_1, B_2 and A_2, B_3 and A_3 and B_4 and A_4 would be in equilibrium. This is clearly an approximation. In theory, it takes an infinite amount of time to establish phase equilibria. In practice, the time of contact between phases is finite.

1. *Stage Efficiency.* It is necessary to divide the calculated number of ideal thermodynamic stages by an efficiency factor to arrive at a realistic and operable design. The efficiency factor will depend on (*a*) residence time in the stage and (*b*) effectiveness of the contacting device. In general, the design procedure involves calculating the theoretical number of contacts necessary to achieve the required separation and then dividing by a semi-empirical stage efficiency to get the actual number of stages required. For example,

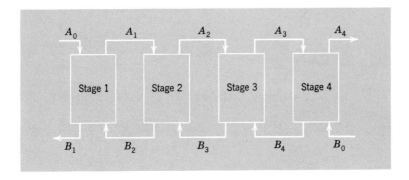

FIG. 3–1. Four equilibrium stages with countercurrent flow.

if it is calculated that seventy theoretical contacts are required to achieve a specified separation, and an efficiency of 70 % is anticipated in each ideal stage, one hundred contacting units would be required.

2. *Throughput.* The fact that seventy theoretical stages were required to achieve the specified separation is dictated by the equilibrium relationships involved. This number of stages is required whether the equipment is to process one pound or a million pounds per year. Although the *number of stages* would not vary, the *physical dimensions* of each stage must vary directly with the amount of material processed, the physical dimensions being a function of the rate of approach to equilibrium. The defining rate equation may be the rate of mass, heat, or momentum transfer, or a combination of all three. Let us say, for instance, that pressure drop considerations dictate that the vapor velocity in a stage cannot exceed 1 foot per second. If the vapor density is 0.1 lb/cu ft, a stage can handle a mass flux of (1 ft/sec)(0.1 lb/cu ft) = 0.1 lb/sec sq ft, and we have established the diameter of the stage as a function of throughput. If a throughput of 10 lb/sec is specified, the stage area would then be (10 lb/sec)/(0.1 lb/sec sq ft), or 100 sq ft.

3. *Contact Time.* For complete specification of size, a height as well as a diameter is needed. Often the height of the stage will be dictated by mass transfer considerations. If 1 second is required for the streams to come to equilibrium at the specified velocity of 1 ft/sec, then the height of the stage is 1 ft.

If the separation is a very difficult one, as many as several hundred stages may be required to accomplish a desired separation. Clearly, the cost of building several hundred individual contacts and operating them in series would be inordinate. The major mechanical design problem thus consists of simulating the action of many individual contacts in a single piece of equipment.

A commonly used arrangement for building multiple staging into one vertical apparatus is shown in Fig. 3–2, which represents two stages of a distillation column. The liquid enters through the downcomer *A*, flows across the perforated plate *B*, and onto the next perforated plate (stage 2) via downcomer *C*.[1] The vapor flows countercurrent to the liquid. It passes through the holes in the perforated plate, mass transfer between the vapor and liquid being

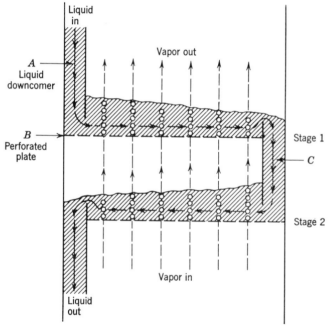

FIG. 3–2. A two-stage sieve plate unit.

[1] Some stage designs omit the downcomer, the liquid and vapor passing each other through the same perforations.

accomplished within the bulk liquid on the plate. Design of a multi-stage column of this type is a difficult design problem. There must be a sufficient depth of liquid on the plate to assure good contact between the gas and liquid, and yet the pressure drop through the plates must be sufficient to prevent the flow of liquid through the perforations (a condition known as "weeping"). If the equipment is poorly designed, the liquid will run down through the plates instead of through the downcomers and, in extreme cases, never will mix with the vapor. This condition is called channeling or short-circuiting.

The column in Fig. 3–2 is an example of an apparatus which duplicates the action of the individual stages of Fig. 3–1. In each stage two phases in countercurrent flow are contacted, and then disengaged.

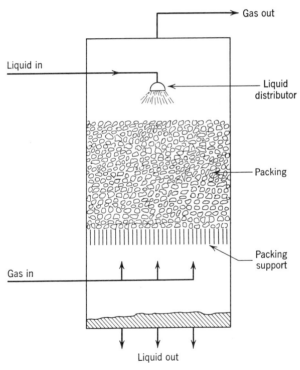

FIG. 3–3. A packed column.

It is possible to carry out a multi-stage operation without disengaging the phases, except at the ends of the apparatus. Figure 3–3 is a schematic representation of a packed column. Here a vapor flows countercurrent to the downward-flowing liquid. The job of the packing is to provide mixing and to afford surface area for contact. Again we note that several types of malfunctioning are possible. If the liquid runs down the walls, and the gas flows up the center of the column, the two phases will not mix—a condition known as "channeling." If the vapor flow is too high, liquid will be blown out the top; if the liquid flow is too high, the liquid rather than gas phase becomes continuous, a condition known as "flooding."

The packed column is a differential device, there being no physically distinguishable stages. We can, however, determine the length of column which gives the same separation as a theoretical stage. If, for instance, a 70-foot high column gives a separation equivalent to a seventy-stage countercurrent cascade,[1] 1 foot of column would, on the average, "equal" one theoretical stage.

3-3 TYPICAL EQUIPMENT—DISTILLATION

Distillation is normally the cheapest method for separating the components of a homogeneous liquid phase, no reagent other than energy being required. A well-designed column will separate components whose difference in boiling points is as close as 4 degrees. If the system forms an azeotrope, or is difficult to distill for other reasons, this problem frequently can be circumvented by *azeotropic* or *extractive distillation techniques.*

Figure 3–4 shows the Keyes process for making absolute ethyl alcohol; an example of the separation of a binary azeotrope by heterogeneous azeotropic distillation. Water and alcohol form an azeotrope containing 95.6% by weight alcohol and boiling at 78.15°C at 1 atm. Thus it is impossible to obtain absolute alcohol (b.p. 78.40°C) by direct distillation. The addition of benzene to the alcohol-water azeotrope results in the formation of a ternary azeotrope, containing 18.5% alcohol, 74.1% benzene, and 7.4% water, and boiling at 64.85°C. Upon condensation, the ternary azeotrope separates into two layers: a top layer containing 14.5% alcohol, 84.5% benzene, and 1% water, and a bottom layer of 53% alcohol, 11% benzene and 36% water. Each of these layers can

---

[1] A series of stages is termed a "cascade."

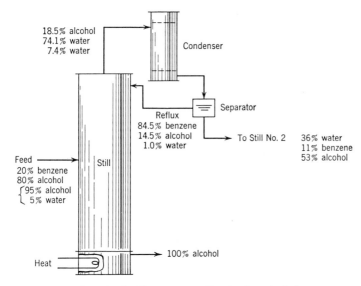

FIG. 3–4. The Keyes process for absolute alcohol.

now be further purified while the absolute alcohol, which has a boiling point above that of the ternary azeotrope, is recovered from the bottom of the column. Similar azeotropic distillation schemes are widely used in the separation of closely boiling hydrocarbon systems.

Extractive distillations, like azeotropic distillations, depend on the addition of a third component. The major difference between the two processes is a matter of nomenclature. In the former case the added component is relatively non-volatile and goes out with the bottoms; in the latter, as in the Keyes process, it goes out with the overhead.

The nomenclature used in connection with distillation columns is shown in Fig. 4–10 on page 80. A multistage unit of this type where there is a cascade above and below the feed point is also called a *fractionating column*. The feed enters on stage f, the stages above the feed, n to $f + 1$, comprise the so-called *rectification or enriching section* of the column, and those below the feed ($f - 1$ to m) the *stripping section*. The top condenser is called a *total condenser* if the entire vapor stream, V, is condensed, in which case the product is liquid, as is the L_R, the reflux stream. If the condenser delivers a vapor product and a liquid reflux, it is termed a *partial condenser*. The ratio of reflux rate to product rate is the (external) *reflux ratio*.

3-4 *VAPOR-LIQUID CONTACTING IN TRAY COLUMNS*

In the usual "tray"-type distillation column, the liquid flows across a horizontal plate (tray) and the vapor is forced to bubble through it, as in Fig. 3–2, a schematic layout of a *sieve plate unit*. Such units can be constructed with or without liquid downcomers. More prevalent than sieve plates are the so-called *bubble cap plates*. Figure 3–5 is a cross-sectional view of this type of plate; Fig. 3–6 shows typical bubble caps and risers.

The essential parts of a bubble cap are the cup-shaped cap and the chimney riser. The vapor travels up the riser and is forced through the slots in the cap. The downcomer weir (Fig. 3–5) holds the liquid level above the slots of the cap, thus assuring good liquid-vapor contact. The riser prevents the liquid from dumping through the cap.

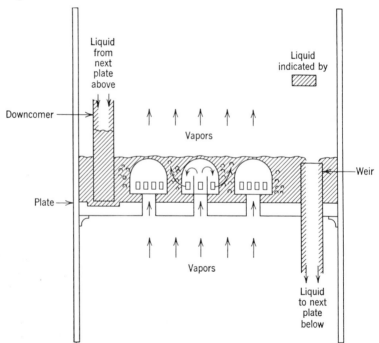

FIG. 3–5. Cross section of a bubble cap plate.

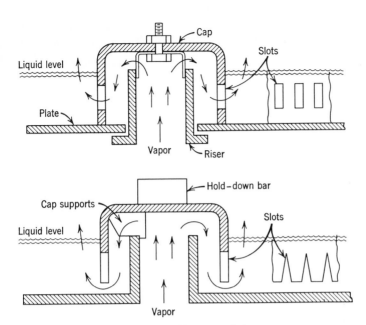

FIG. 3–6. Bubble caps and risers.

Some of the design parameters are:

1. *Plate spacing.* The minimum spacing between plates is determined by the height of liquid on the plate required to balance the pressure drop of the vapor across the plate. In bubble cap columns the spacings are usually 6 in. to 3 ft, a certain height above the liquid surface being required to disengage the two phases.

2. *Limiting Vapor Velocity.* If the vapor velocity is too large, liquid will be entrained in the vapor, and in an extreme case, the liquid will be blown off the plate and the liquid seal about the base of the bubble cap will be lost; hence no vapor-liquid contact will take place. Alternatively, an excessive vapor velocity can cause a high pressure drop across the plate, preventing the liquid phase from passing down the column.

If the flow of liquid down the tower is impeded by excessive entrainment or pressure drop, this condition is referred to as *flooding.*

3. *Plate Stability.* Ideally, the vapor flows through all the caps, and the liquid height across the plate is relatively level. If excessively

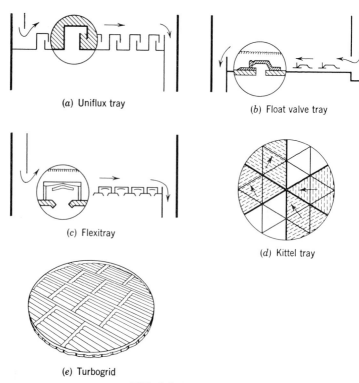

(a) Uniflux tray

(b) Float valve tray

(c) Flexitray

(d) Kittel tray

(e) Turbogrid

FIG. 3–7. Tray designs.

high level gradients occur, the liquid will build up (usually around the downcomer) and force liquid over the risers in the cap and through to the plate below. This condition is known as "dumping." When this condition occurs, the vapor rate is reduced through the caps which are dumping and the vapor channels through the other caps.

4. *Clean Out and Maintenance.* The mechanical designs must be such that the bubble caps and plates can be made accessible for periodic inspections and/or cleanings. Larger columns have manholes for entry. The details of the design depend upon the anticipated maintenance performance of the tower which is a function of the process materials and required operating conditions.

The past ten years have seen a rapid introduction of many new types of tray designs in addition to the sieve, or perforated plate column. Among others, are the trays shown in Fig. 3–7, namely:

(*a*) Uniflux—an inverted L-shaped cap that directs the vapor flow parallel to the liquid.

(*b*) Float valve tray—this utilizes floating pivotal valves.

(*c*) Flexitray—another floating valve concept.

(*d*) Kittel tray—analogous to the Uniflux insofar as it promotes parallel liquid-vapor flow.

(*e*) Turbogrid—a flat grid of parallel slots, which can be used without downcomers.

Most of the new cap-type plates have specific advantages over the conventional bubble caps and are being used more and more frequently. Their use was originally held back by the lack of reliable design data, and to a lesser extent by the fact that the originators of the trays receive royalties averaging about $1 per square foot.

The sieve plate, which is one of the least expensive trays, is now supplanting the bubble cap trays in many applications. In addition to representing a 25 to 50% lower initial investment in plates, in many applications, sieve and perforated plates have higher efficiencies than bubble cap trays. Disadvantages are: the immediate dumping of liquid if the gas flow decreases momentarily; a slightly smaller operating capacity range where the efficiency is maintained; change in hole size due to corrosion and fouling; and the close tolerance requirements on plate leveling.

A number of these factors are summarized on pages 44 and 45 in Table 3–1 and Fig. 3–8, which offer a comparison of several types of trays with bubble trays, and packed columns.

3–5 VAPOR-LIQUID CONTACTING IN PACKED COLUMNS

The packed column discussed in Section 3–2 and shown in Fig. 3–3 consists essentially of a vertical shell filled with a packing material.

The function of the packing is to increase the turbulence and surface of contact between phases, and to provide a tortuous path to prevent by-passing. In addition to corrosion and structural requirements, packing materials should provide a large free volume (to reduce pressure drop) and have a low density and cost. Hence almost any conceivable shape and substance can be used.

In some applications broken rock or coke are suitable, however

TABLE 3–1

COMPARISON OF SEVERAL TYPES OF TRAYS WITH THE BUBBLE TRAY[1]

Type	Vapor Capacity Relative to Bubble Tray	Efficiency		Dirty Service Performance	Tray ΔP Relative to Bubble Tray	Cost Relative to Bubble Tray
		Range of High Efficiency	Relative to Bubble Tray			
No liquid down-comers Turbogrid Ripple tray	20–40% greater	Relatively narrow Poor at low vapor load	Approx. same at 60–80% of flood or above, less at lower vapor rates	Good	Low For turbogrid about $\frac{1}{3}$ at 60–100% of flooding	$\frac{1}{2}$
Valve type Flexitray	20–50% greater	Wide (20–85% of flooding)	5–10% higher at optimum	Good	Slightly lower at high vapor rates	$\frac{2}{3}$
Uniflux	10–20% greater	Relatively wide, good above 50% of flooding	10% higher at optimum	Questionable	Low	$\frac{1}{2}$
Sieve trays $\frac{1}{16}$- to $\frac{1}{4}$-in. holes	20–40% greater	Relatively wide	Approx. 10% higher	Poor	Low	$\frac{2}{3}$

[1] Gerster, J. A., *Chem. Eng. Prog.*, **59**, No. 3, 35 (1963), from Fryback, M. G., and J. A. Hufnagel, *Ind. Eng. Chem.*, **52**, 654 (1960).

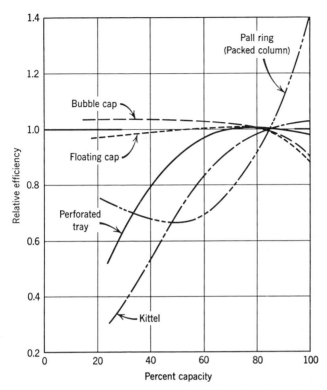

FIG. 3–8. Efficiency of various contactors as a function of capacity, relative to the efficiency of 85% of capacity. (Gerster, *op. cit.*)

more sophisticated geometric shapes provide higher contacting efficiency. Figure 3–9 shows some of the common shapes of tower packing available commercially. Of the ones shown, the Raschig rings have found the most widespread use. They are relatively inexpensive, available in many sizes and from many vendors, and performance data are available. They provide the required free volume and effective surface of contact to accomplish a multistage distillation.

Design methods for packed columns involve a high degree of empiricism. The flow parameters are difficult to define analytically and physical variables, such as effective column volume and interfacial areas, are either unknown or difficult to measure. In general,

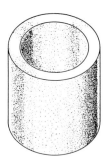

Raschig ring

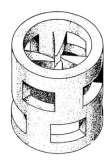

Pall ring

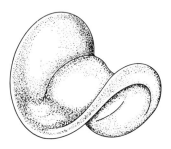

Berl saddle

Intalox saddle

FIG. 3–9. Tower packings.

the design methods involve utilization of performance data furnished by the manufacturers of the packing materials.

Because plate columns and packed columns are competitive for many applications, it is interesting to compare their relative merits. Some of the advantages enjoyed by packed columns are that they:

1. Are usually less expensive.
2. Give good service in some corrosive conditions because ceramic packing can be used.
3. Generally have lower pressure drops.
4. Usually have lower liquid hold up.
5. Are relatively unaffected by foaming.

On the other hand, they:
1. Are difficult to clean.
2. Are generally heavier than plate columns.
3. Cannot be internally heated or cooled.
4. Are subject to channeling.

Although one can construct plate columns up to 30 ft in diameter, large diameter packed columns perform badly because the liquid tends to flow down the walls while the gas passes upward through the center. This necessitates installing troughs or distributors at intervals of, on the average, every 8 ft in columns of more than 8 to 12 in. in diameter. Also, in the taller columns it is customary to re-support the packing every 8 to 12 ft, to avoid crushing the packing at the bottom, and to stack the packing carefully. Under these conditions, the economic advantages of a packed column begin to vanish.

3–6 GAS ABSORPTION PROCESSES

Gas absorption is used to recover a valuable constituent in a gas stream, or to remove an objectionable one. There are many parallels between absorption and distillation, both processes involving the contacting of vapors and liquids. The primary difference is that, unlike distillation, absorption does not involve repeated condensations and evaporations. An interesting operation which has the characteristics of both distillation and absorption is *stripping*. Here an inert carrier gas is used to remove a dissolved gas or very volatile component from a liquid.

Some examples of gas absorption operations are given in Table 3–2.

3–7 GAS ABSORPTION EQUIPMENT

In the absence of chemical reaction, the solubility of most gases in liquids is low, particularly if the gases are near or above their critical points. Since most gas absorptions are followed by heating cycles in which the absorbed gas is recovered, methods must be developed to obtain high concentrations of gas in the liquid. This is done by choosing a solvent which reacts with the gas to form a thermally unstable chemical compound. Thus the liquid absorbent will have a strong affinity for the gas, and relatively few stages are required to achieve useful separations.

Because of the relatively few stages required, the simpler packed column is preferred to the plate column for most gas absorption

TABLE 3–2

SOME INDUSTRIAL APPLICATIONS OF GAS ABSORPTION

Gas Stream	Material Absorbed	Solvent	Purpose
Light hydro-carbons	Butane, propane	Kerosene	Recovery
Stack gas	SO_2	Aromatic amines, ammonia, bisulfites	Removal
Coal gas, refinery gas	NH_3	Water, acids	Removal
Coal gas	Pyridine	Ammonia solution	Recovery
Natural gas	Water	Glycol, $CaCl_2$, lithium halides	Removal
Synthetic gas	CO	Copper-ammonia salt, H_2O, alkaline solids	Removal
Refinery gas, coal gas	H_2	Liquid N_2	Recovery
Refinery gas, coal gas	H_2S	Aqueous bases, water, and alco-holic amines	Removal & Recovery
Refinery gas, coal gas	CO_2	Aqueous bases, water, and alco-holic amines	Removal & Recovery
Coal gas	Benzene	Gas oil or straw oil	Recovery
Coal gas	Naphthalene	Oil	Recovery
Exhaust gases	HF, SiF_4	Water	Removal
HCl	HCl	Water	Acid manufacture
Exhaust gas	Cl_2, HCl	Water	Removal
SO_3	SO_3	Aqueous H_2SO_4	Acid manufacture

operations. Furthermore, packed columns have inherently lower pressure drops than plate columns. This is relatively unimportant in most distillations, but in gas absorption high pressure drops necessitate purchase of expensive gas compressors. If very large volumes of gases need to be handled, or very high columns are required, plate type installations are usually specified, since the efficiency of a plate column goes up with diameter while that of a packed column goes down.

In many gas absorption applications, such as the absorption of SiF_4 by water, the solvent has such great affinity for the gas that very few stages are required. In this case one may bubble a gas through an agitated liquid, or use a spray column. The simplest spray absorption column consists of nothing more than an empty chamber in which liquid is sprayed downward and gas enters at the bottom. In the more sophisticated devices both phases may be dispersed through relatively complicated atomization nozzles, pressure nozzles, Venturi atomizers, or jets.

Spray units have the advantage of a low gas pressure drop; they will not plug should solids form, and they never flood.

3–7 ADSORPTION

Until very recently the use of adsorption systems was generally limited to the adsorption of a small percentage (generally less than 10%) of the components of a stream. Recent progress in materials and engineering techniques has greatly extended the applications, as attested by Table 3–3,[1] which lists only those applications that have been commercialized. The adsorbents used in effecting these separations are activated carbon, aluminum oxide, silica gel, or synthetic, sodium or calcium alumino-silicate zeolite adsorbents (molecular sieves). The sieves differ from the other adsorbents in that they are crystalline and have pore openings of fixed dimensions.

Adsorption units range from the very simple to the very complex. A simple set-up consists of little more than a cylindrical vessel containing an adsorbent through which the gas or liquid flows. *Regeneration* is accomplished by passing a hot gas through the vessel, usually in the opposite direction to the adsorbent. Normally two vessels are used, one vessel desorbing while the other one adsorbs. If the vessel is arranged vertically, it is usually advantageous

[1] H. M. Barry, *Chemical Engineering*, **67**, No. 3, 105 (1960).

TABLE 3-3

IMPORTANT COMMERCIAL ADSORPTIVE SEPARATIONS

Dehydration Processes		Miscellaneous Separations and Purifications	
(Gases)	(Liquids)	Material Adsorbed	From
Acetylene	Acetone	Acetylene	Liquid oxygen
Air	Acetonitrile	Ammonia	Cracked ammonia
Argon	Acrylonitrile	Ammonia	Reformer hydrogen
Carbon dioxide	Allyl chloride	2-Butyne	Isoprene
Chlorine	Benzene	Carbon dioxide	Ethylene
Cracked gas	Butadiene	Carbon dioxide	Air
Ethylene	n-Butane	Carbon dioxide	Inert gases
Helium	Butene	Carbon monoxide, methane	Hydrogen
Hydrogen	Butyl acetate		
Hydrogen chloride	Carbon tetrachloride	Compressor oil	Many kinds of gases
Hydrogen sulfide	Cyclohexane	Cyclic hydrocarbons	Naphthenes and paraffins
Natural gas	Dichloroethylene	Ethanol	Diethyl ether
Nitrogen	Di-methyl sulfoxide	Gasoline components	Natural gas
Oxygen	Ethanol	Hydrogen sulfide	Liquefied petroleum gas
Reformer hydrogen	Ethylene dibromide	Hydrogen sulfide	Natural gas
Sulfur hexafluoride	Ethylene dichloride	Hydrogen sulfide	Reformer hydrogen
	No. 2 fuel oil	Krypton	Hydrogen
	n-Heptane	Mercaptans	Propane
	n-Hexane	Methanol	Diethyl ether
	Isoprene	Methylene chloride	Refrigerant 114
	Isopropanol	Nitrogen	Hydrogen
	Jet, fuel,	NO, NO$_2$, N$_2$O	Nitrogen
	Liquefied petroleum gas	Oil vapor	Compressed gases
	Methyl chloride	Oxygen	Argon
	Mixed ethyl ketone	Unsaturates	Diethyl ether
	Etc.		

to employ downward flow to prevent bed-lift. Lift causes particle attrition which, in turn, increases pressure drop and the loss of material.

Although regeneration is usually accomplished by thermal cycle, pressure cycles (desorption by decompression), purge-gas cycles (desorption by partial pressure lowering), and displacement cycles (addition of a third component) are also used.

3-8 EXTRACTION—LIQUID-LIQUID

Liquid-liquid extraction is directly competitive with distillation, both processes involving the separation of components of a homogeneous liquid. Inspection of Table 3-4, which lists some of the

TABLE 3-4

TYPICAL COMMERCIAL EXTRACTION PROCESSES

Solute	Solvent	Process
Sulfur compounds or mercaptans	Caustic soda	Petroleum sweetening
Aromatics	SO_2, diethyl, glycol	Petroleum de-aromatization
Petroleum fractions	Furfural, nitrobenzene, ether	Remove gum formers
Lube oils	Propane	Remove paraffins
Tallow	Propane	Decolorization
Animal oils	Propane, furfural	Vitamin recovery
Abietic acid	Naphtha	Rosin refining
Penicillin	Amyl acetate	Recovery
Bacitracin	Butanol	Recovery
Acetic acid	Ethyl acetate	Cellulose acetate manufacture
Salt	Ammonia	Caustic purification
Phenol	Benzene	Raschig process
Aniline	Nitrobenzene	Recovery from water
Uranium nitrate	Tributyl phosphate	Uranium recovery

more common extraction processes, shows that extraction is preferred to distillation in a number of instances. For example:

1. In the case of dissolved solids, volatilization may be impractical.
2. In dilute solutions, if the desired component has the lower

vapor pressure, the heat requirement for distillation may render that process non-competitive, as in the recovery of acetic acid in cellulose acetate manufacture.

TABLE 3–5

PERFORMANCE OF COMMERCIAL EXTRACTION EQUIPMENT

Equipment	Liquid Capacity, Combined Streams, cu ft/(sq ft)(hr)	Stage Spacing	Stage Efficiency	Typical Applications
Mixer-settler	—	1 stage/unit	75–100%	Duo-Sol lube oil process
Spray column	50–250	—	—	NaCl from NaOH using NH_3 (Aq.)
Packed column	20–150	—	—	Phenol recovery
Perforated-plate column	10–200	6–24 in.	30% for 4–8 in. plate spacing	Furfural lube oil process
Koch column	10–200	16 in.	20–75%	Gasoline desulfurization
Baffle column	60–105	4–6 in.	5–10%	Acetic acid recovery
Bubble cap column	—	12 in.	5–10%	—
York-Scheibel column	50–100	1–2 ft mixer unit	80–100%	Pharmaceuticals and organic chemicals
Podbielniak	To 20,000 gal/hr 1000–5000 gal/hr		—	Antibiotics
Luwesta	3800 gal/hr		—	Penicillin extraction

3. For the removal of a specific component, such as the color former in tallow, or mercaptans in petroleum, solvent extraction is competitive with adsorption rather than distillation.

4. In the recovery of heat sensitive substances, extraction also competes with adsorption or ion exchange rather than distillation.

A schematic portrayal of an extraction process is found in Fig. 7–20 on page 133. The nomenclature here is quite similar to that used in distillation, with the solvent being the analog of heat. The "solvent separator" is usually a distillation column.

The key to carrying out an effective extraction lies with the choice of a suitable solvent. In addition to being non-toxic, inexpensive, and non-flammable, a good solvent must be essentially immiscible with the raffinate stream, and have a different density. It must also have a very high affinity for the solute, from which it should be easily separated by distillation, crystallization, or other means.

If the solvent is a good one, the distribution coefficient for the solute between the phases will be at least five, and perhaps as much as fifty. Under these circumstances, an extraction column will not require many stages, and this indeed is usually the case (see Example 1–1).

Since not very many stages are required, in addition to using packed or spray towers, one can consider using more complicated equipment such as sieve plates with mechanical agitation between the trays, high speed rotating equipment, or a series of individual mixer-settlers. Table 3–5 lists some of the performance characteristics of the various types of units employed.[1]

The mixer-settler unit is shown in Fig. 3–10. The disc and doughnut column of Fig. 3–11 is a typical baffled column. Figure 3–12 is the York-Scheibel unit. Figure 3–13 is a similar unit, developed by the Shell Company and called a rotating disc contactor. Figures 3–14 and 3–15 depict the Podbielniak and Luwesta machines. Detailed descriptions of these units are given in von Berg,[1] Treybal,[2] or Sherwood and Pigford.[3]

The choice of unit will be dictated by economics; in general, the more difficult the separation, the more expensive the unit which must be used. Special problems are presented by materials that are easily emulsified, have small density differences, or are corrosive. It is of interest to note that the best mass transfer is obtained during the initial dispersion of the two liquid phases. This accounts for the high efficiency of the York-Scheibel, Koch, and mixer-settler units, which have disengaging sections between the contacts. Baffled

[1] von Berg, R. L., and H. Wiegand, *Chemical Engineering*, p. 189 (June 1952).

[2] Treybal, R. E., *Liquid Extraction*, McGraw-Hill Book Co., New York, 1950.

[3] Sherwood, T., and R. Pigford, *Adsorption and Extraction*, 2nd ed., McGraw-Hill Book Co., New York, 1952.

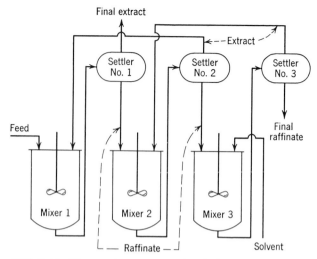

FIG. 3–10. Mixer-settler system run batchwise or continuously.

columns and spray columns have low efficiencies, but are preferred in cases where emulsions may form or solids may deposit.

In general the efficiency of an extraction column is increased by agitating the liquid in the column. One method of doing this is by circulating the liquids through piston pumps placed at the base of

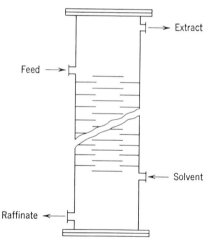

FIG. 3–11. Disc and doughnut column.

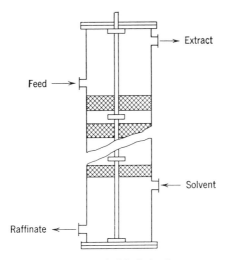

FIG. 3–12. York-Scheibel column.

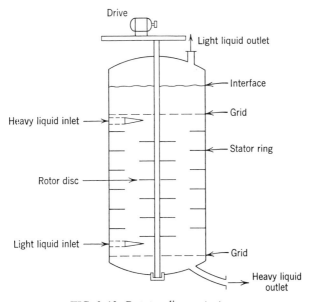

FIG. 3–13. Rotator disc contactor.

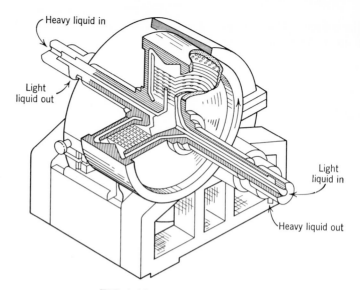

FIG. 3–14. Podbielniak extractor.

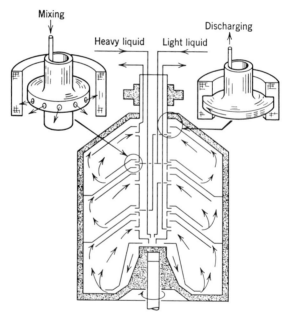

FIG. 3–15. Luwesta extractor.

the column. These are pulsed to give 3 to 10 pulsations per minute with stroke amplitudes of about $\frac{1}{4}$ inch.

3-9 EXTRACTION—SOLID-LIQUID (LEACHING)

Solid-liquid extractions are widely used in the metallurgical, natural product, and food industries. Leaching is done under batch, semi-batch, or continuous operating conditions, in stagewise or continuous-contact equipment.

The major problem in leaching is to promote diffusion of the solute out of the solid and into the liquid. The most effective way of doing this is to reduce the solid to the smallest possible size that is economically feasible, thus reducing the solid diffusion path. Size reduction is very costly because it consumes large amounts of power.

For large-scale applications, in the metallurgical industries in particular, large open tanks are used in countercurrent operation such as the one shown in Fig. 3–10. The major difference between the solid-liquid and liquid-liquid systems centers about the difficulty of transporting the solid, or the solid slurry, from stage to stage. For this reason the solid is often left in the same tank, and only the liquid is transferred from tank to tank.

In the pharmaceutical, food, and natural product industries countercurrent solid transport is often provided by fairly complicated mechanical devices. Some of the extractors available are the Rotocel, Kennedy, Hildebandt, Miag, Dexter, Bellman, and Benotto designs. Most of these are little more than sophisticated screw conveyors. Figure 3–16 shows a typical rotating blade extraction unit.

3-10 ION EXCHANGE

In contrast to most unit operations, which date back to Biblical times, the principles of ion exchange were not known until the 1800's. Today ion exchange is a major industrial operation, largely because of its wide-scale use in water softening. Numerous other ion exchange processes are also in use. Some of these are listed in Table 3–6.

Ion exchange resembles gas adsorption and liquid-liquid extraction in that in all these processes an inert carrier is employed, and the reagent used to selectively remove a component must be regenerated. In a typical ion exchange application, water softening,

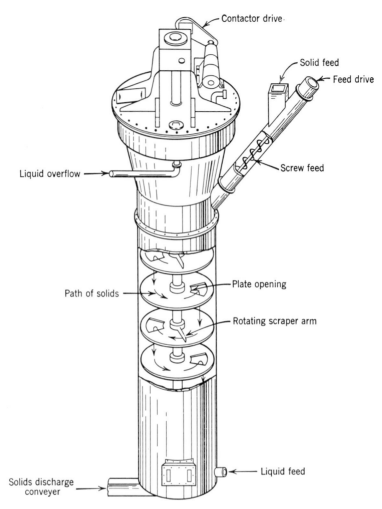

FIG. 3–16. Rotating-blade column for countercurrent contact of a liquid and a solid phase.

an organic or inorganic polymer in its sodium form removes calcium ions by exchanging calcium for sodium. After prolonged use the (spent) polymer, which is now saturated with calcium, is regenerated by contact with a concentrated brine, the law of mass action governing the degree of regeneration.

TABLE 3-6

APPLICATIONS OF ION EXCHANGE

Process	Material Exchanged	Purpose
Water treatment	Calcium ions	Removal
Water de-alkylization	Dicarbonate	Removal
Aluminum anodization bath	Aluminum	Removal
Plating baths	Metals	Recovery
Rayon wastes	Copper	Recovery
Glycerine	Sodium chloride	Removal
Wood pulping	Sulfate liquor	Recovery
Formaldehyde manufacture	Formic acid	Recovery
Ethylene glycol (from oxide)	Glycol	Catalysis
Sugar solution	Ash	Removal
Grapefruit processing	Pectin	Recovery

Among the many factors entering into the design of industrial exchangers are the problems of:

1. *Channeling.* The problem of non-uniform flow distribution and subsequent by-pass is generic to all types of flow operations.

2. *Loss of Resins.* Ultimately, the exchange capacity of the resin will diminish to the point where it can no longer be used. Resins being rather expensive reagents, this constitutes a major cost item. In a system where the resin is recirculated, loss by attrition is superimposed on the other losses, which also include cracking of the resin by osmotic pressure.

3. *Resin Utilization.* This is the ratio of the quantity of ions removed during treatment to the total capacity of the resin; it must be maximized.

4. *Pressure Drop.* The exchange being very fast, the limiting rate step is often the diffusion into the resin. To overcome this diffusional resistance, the resin size must be reduced and the liquid flow rate increased. Both of these measures result in an increased pressure drop and increased pumping costs.

The methods of operation used reflect the efforts to overcome these design problems. Ion exchange units are built to operate batchwise (a fixed amount of resin and liquid are mixed together), or as fixed-beds where the solution is pumped through a bed of resin, or as continuous countercurrent contactors. In general, fixed beds are preferred where high purities and recoveries are desired; batch processes are advantageous where very favorable equilibriums exist or slurries must be handled; continuous countercurrent operation offers more effective utilization of regeneration chemicals, and geometric compactness.

One of the more interesting methods for continuous counter-current ion exchange is the use of *fluidized bed* techniques for continuous circulation of the resin. Figure 3–17 shows the Dorr Company's "Hydro-softener." In a fluidized bed a solid phase is suspended in a liquid or gas. Consequently, the solid behaves like a fluid and can be pumped, gravity-fed, and handled very much like a liquid.

In the "Hydro-softener" shown, the fluidized resin moves down through the softener on the right, and is then picked up by a brine-carrier fluid and transferred to the regenerator on the left. The operation in both the absorber and regenerator is truly counter-current.

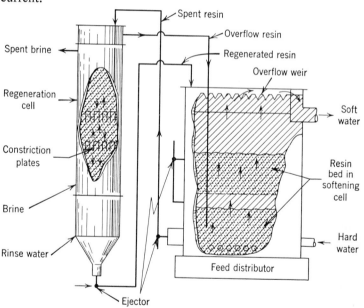

FIG. 3–17. Dorrco "Hydro-softener" for water.

Since many chemicals are processed wet and sold dry, one of the manufacturing operations must be a *drying operation* (the removal of a liquid from a solid by vaporization of the liquid). Although the only basic requirement in drying is that the vapor pressure of the liquid to be evaporated be higher than its partial pressure in the gas stream, the design and operation of driers represent complex problems in heat transfer, fluid flow, and mass transfer. In addition to the effect of external conditions of temperature, humidity, air flow, state of subdivision, etc., on the drying rate, the internal conditions of liquid diffusion, capillary flow, equilibrium moisture content, and heat sensitivity must be considered. In practice these internal conditions vary during the course of a drying process.

Factors in the design of a dryer are:

1. *Thermal Stability of Substrate.*   In general, the hotter the gas, the faster and the more efficient the drying. Temperatures of most drying operations are usually limited by the thermal stability of the solid.

2. *Gas Properties.*   If the temperature of the gas is above the boiling point of the liquid to be removed, there is no problem. In low-temperature drying, however, dehumidification of drying medium may be required.

3. *Heat Transfer.*   Because heat transfer through solids is mostly by conduction, this, rather than convective or radiative heat transfer in the gas, becomes the limiting heat-transfer rate step.

4. *Heating Medium.*   Direct heating by steam-heated air, combustion products, or superheated vapor may be employed. Alternatively, indirect heating of the solid through a retaining wall or by infrared radiation can be employed.

5. *Diffusion.*   The problem here is analogous to the one described in 3, most of the resistance to diffusion occurring in the solid phase. Usually, during the early stages of a drying operation, heat transfer is the limiting rate step; in the later stages, mass transfer becomes the controlling factor.

Evaporation is generally defined as the removal of a liquid from a liquid phase into a (pure) gas phase by volatilization. Of the factors cited as being important in drying, only one and two are of importance in evaporation, the resistance to heat transfer and diffusion occurring primarily in the gas phase.

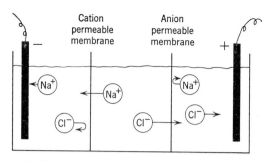

FIG. 3–18. Principle of three-compartment electrodialysis cells.

3–12 LESS COMMON AND NEW TECHNIQUES

1. *Dialysis.* This involves the separation of substances in liquid solutions by virtue of different rates of diffusion through membranes. The process is infrequently used because it is intrinsically slow, and because membranes having sufficiently high selectivity are not available. The most important application is the separation of sodium hydroxide from the hemi-cellulose in the viscose-rayon process.

2. *Electromembrane Ion Exchange (Electrodialysis).* The principle of operation of a multi-compartmented electrodialysis unit is shown in Fig. 3–18. The cation and anion permeable membranes carry fixed charges; thus they prevent the migration of species of like charge. In a commercial version of Fig. 3–17, there would be several hundred rather than three compartments, multi-compartmentalization being required to achieve electric power economies, since electrolysis takes place at the electrodes. The purification of brackish salt water is the major current use of electrodialysis.

3. *Gaseous Diffusion.* For a gas flowing through a barrier having very small holes, the rate of flow is inversely proportional to the molecular weight of the gas. The process is slow, and pumping costs are enormous.

4. *Other Techniques.* ATMOLYSIS—Countercurrent diffusion of a component of a gas stream into another gas. THERMAL DIFFUSION—Preferential diffusion of molecules under a temperature gradient. FOAM SEPARATION—Removal of a surface-active material from a homogeneous solution by adsorbing it on a gas bubble (foam). ZONE REFINING—Uni-directional melting in such a fashion that the impurities pass into the (moving) liquid boundary. ION EXCLUSION—Separation of ionized from non-ionized substances by their relative rates of passage through an ion exchange column.

four / graphical design methods—
McCabe-Thiele

Graphical methods are exceedingly useful for presenting a visualization of the interrelationships among a set of variables, and as such are commonly used in chemical engineering. Their utility in stagewise contactor design stems from the fact that the design involves the simultaneous solution of equilibrium relationships along with material and energy balances. The equilibrium relationships, being complex functions of the system properties, are usually presented in the graphical forms discussed in Chapter 2. Hence it is convenient to plot the material and energy balance equations on the same graph. By proper choice of coordinates and appropriate geometric constructions, it is then possible to achieve simple graphical solutions to involved problems. It is, of course, true that any problem amenable to solution by graphical techniques can also be handled analytically. In fact, the increasing availability of high-speed computing facilities is rapidly antiquating classical graphical design methods. However, they remain useful for preliminary designs, and for on-stream process analysis.

4-1 COUNTERCURRENT MULTI-STAGE CONTACTING

In a countercurrent multi-stage operation, the phases to be contacted enter a series of ideal or equilibrium stages from opposite ends. A contactor of this type is diagramatically represented by Fig. 4–1.

When a multi-stage contacting device of this type is used, between each equilibrium stage there must always be two passing streams, one entering and one leaving the contact. In Fig. 4–1, which may be visualized as a distillation, absorption, or extraction column, the stages represent points of equilibrium between the two phases being contacted. V and L are the mass of the two phases; x and y are the mass fraction compositions of phases L and V, respectively; and

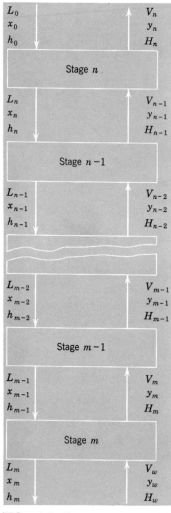

h and H are the enthalpy per unit mass of phases L and V, respectively. The mass units may be g, lb, g mole, lb mole, etc.

Considering stage $n - 1$ as an example, the mass L_n of phase L from stage n, is contacted with phase V from stage $n - 2$, V_{n-2}. The two streams are equilibrated, separated, and then discharged from the ideal stage, with phase L_{n-1} in equilibrium with phase V_{n-1}.

Considering the entire series of equilibrium stages at steady state, over-all material and energy balances give the following:

For the total balance, mass in = mass out, or

$$V_w + L_0 = V_n + L_m \quad (4\text{--}1)$$

An over-all component balance may also be written; if there are two components, A and B, the total mass balance of component A,

$$V_w y_{wA} + L_0 x_{0A} = V_n y_{nA} + L_m x_{mA} \quad (4\text{--}2)$$

where subscript A refers to the A component.

Similarly, an energy balance may be written for the entire series of stages. If kinetic energy and elevation effects are negligible and

FIG. 4–1. Countercurrent multistage contactor.

the operation is conducted adiabatically at constant pressure, an enthalpy balance constitutes a total energy balance.

$$V_w H_w + L_0 h_0 = V_n H_n + L_m H_m \qquad (4\text{--}3)$$

A component balance can be made for each stage. If there are only two components, x may be used to denote mass fraction of component A in phase L, and y in phase V, and the subscript A may be dropped.[1] A balance for component A about stage n is:

$$L_0 x_0 + V_{n-1} y_{n-1} = V_n y_n + L_n x_n \qquad (4\text{--}4)$$

A relationship between the two passing streams L_n and V_{n-1}, which can be plotted on an x-y equilibrium diagram, may be obtained by rewriting Eq. 4–4:

$$y_{n-1} = \frac{L_n}{V_{n-1}} (x_n) + \frac{V_n y_n - L_0 x_0}{V_{n-1}} \qquad (4\text{--}5)$$

A similar material balance between stage $n-1$ and the top of the column may be made:

$$L_0 x_0 + V_{n-2} y_{n-2} = V_n y_n + L_{n-1} x_{n-1} \qquad (4\text{--}4a)$$

Solving for y_{n-2}, we obtain

$$y_{n-2} = \frac{L_{n-1}}{V_{n-2}} x_{n-1} + \frac{V_n y_n - L_0 x_0}{V_{n-2}} \qquad (4\text{--}5a)$$

Equations 4–5 and 4–5a define two sets of points (y_{n-1}, x_n) and (y_{n-2}, x_{n-1}) on a line on an x-y diagram, the line being called the *operating line*. *All* passing streams in the column, (L_0, V_n), (V_{n-1}, L_n), (V_{n-2}, L_{n-1}), etc., can be located on the same operating line, which may be curved or straight. Equations such as 4–5, in addition to locating passing streams on an x-y diagram, also establish the slope of the operating line L_{n-1}/V_{n-2} between stages $n-1$ and $n-2$ and its intercept $(V_n y_n - L_0 x_0)/V_{n-2}$. *If* the liquid and vapor flows are constant throughout the column, $L/V = L_{n-1}/V_{n-2} = L_n/V_{n-1} =$ constant. Furthermore, since $(V_n y_n - L_0 x_0)$ is a constant which depends only on external flows, if L/V is constant, all passing

---

[1] Henceforth, for two component systems no subscripts will be used. y and x will denote the mole fractions of that component in a two-component mixture which concentrates in the distillate or extract.

streams lie on the same *straight* operating line which may thus be drawn if we know either:

1. The concentration of only one set of passing streams, and the L/V, the ratio of the phase flow rates in the contactor.

2. The concentrations of any two pairs of passing streams. The two most convenient streams to analyze are those entering and leaving the cascade (L_0, V_n, and L_m, V_w). These points lie at the ends of the operating line.

A relationship between the ratios of the two phases and the composition of passing streams may be developed. If we assume that the flow rates of liquid and vapor are constant, then we may rewrite Eqs. 4–5 and 4–5a as

$$y_{n-1} = \frac{L}{V} x_n + \frac{Vy_n - Lx_0}{V} \tag{4–6}$$

and

$$y_{n-2} = \frac{L}{V} x_{n-1} + \frac{Vy_n - Lx_0}{V} \tag{4–6a}$$

Subtraction of Eqs. 4–6 and 4–6a yields

$$\frac{y_{n-1} - y_{n-2}}{x_n - x_{n-1}} = \frac{L}{V} = \frac{\Delta y}{\Delta x} \tag{4–7}$$

Under the conditions of constant liquid and vapor flow rates, $\Delta y/\Delta x$ may be taken between any set of two stages in the column.

The number of theoretical stages required to effect the transfer of a specified amount of component A from phase L to phase V can be determined by using the operating line and equilibrium curves. An example of a graphical calculation for a simple countercurrent contactor is shown in Fig. 4–2.

For the apparatus shown in (*b*) of Fig. 4–2, assume that the compositions of the entering and discharging streams are the specified points A and B. These are located as (y_w, x_4) and (y_1, x_0) on (*a*) in Fig. 4–2, which also shows the equilibrium curve for the system. If L/V is constant throughout the column, then the straight line connecting point A with point B is the operating line; the locus of *all* passing streams. To determine the number of stages required to achieve the change of composition A to B, we *step off stages* as shown by the staged-line construction. Starting at A, the passing streams under stage 4, we move vertically to the equilibrium curve to

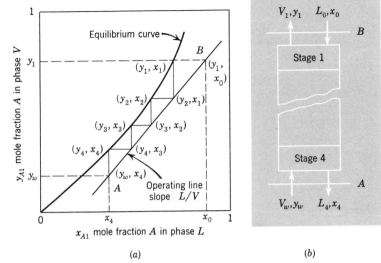

FIG. 4–2. Graphical solution for a two-phase countercurrent contactor.

find y_4, the composition of the vapor leaving stage 4. Next, we move horizontally to the operating line to pick off the point (y_4, x_3), the composition of the passing streams between stages 3 and 4. We continue moving between the passing streams (operating line) to the stages (equilibrium line) until point B is reached. We note that four equilibrium stages were required.

4–2 APPLICATION OF STAGEWISE CALCULATION METHODS TO DISTILLATION—BINARY SYSTEMS

In the application of the principles and equations developed in section 4–1 to distillation design problems, the two phase flows, L and V, represent liquid and vapor respectively. A continuous distillation column is shown in Fig. 4–3.

The vapor phase feed to the bottom of the column provides the energy to maintain a vapor phase rising through the column. The countercurrent liquid phase is provided by condensing the vapor overhead as it leaves the top of the column, and returning a portion of this *distillate* to the top of the column as liquid phase. This returning distillate stream is called *reflux* and the mass ratio of liquid returned per vapor overhead on the top plate is termed the

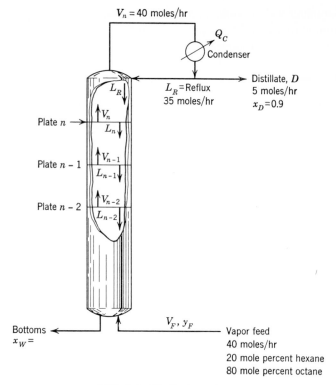

$V_n = 40$ moles/hr

Q_C

Condenser

L_R

$L_R =$ Reflux
35 moles/hr

Distillate, D
5 moles/hr
$x_D = 0.9$

Plate n

V_n
L_n

Plate $n - 1$

V_{n-1}
L_{n-1}

Plate $n - 2$

V_{n-2}
L_{n-2}

Bottoms
$x_W =$

V_F, y_F

Vapor feed
40 moles/hr
20 mole percent hexane
80 mole percent octane

FIG. 4–3. Distillation column.

internal reflux ratio, L_R/V_n. Another way of specifying reflux is on the basis of the *external reflux ratio,* L_R/D.

In the unit depicted in Fig. 4–3, we have 40 lb moles/hr of a vapor feed containing 20% hexane and 80% octane entering the bottom plate and 5 moles/hr of distillate are to be produced. Let us assume that the type of column under consideration is known to operate well with an internal reflux ratio of 0.875 on the top plate. Thus for every one mole of vapor going into the condenser 0.125 mole of liquid distillate is removed, and 0.875 mole of liquid reflux is returned to the top plate. The vapor-liquid equilibrium and enthalpy data for the system hexane-octane are available (Figs. 2–3 and 2–10).

The reflux ratio, feed rates, and feed composition being known, we will postulate that the product specifications call for a distillate containing 90% hexane, and that the number of theoretical plates required to achieve this separation must be calculated.

Before demonstrating the graphical solution, let us examine what is involved in an analytical solution. We proceed by writing mass and energy balances on the basis of 1 hour (40 lb moles of feed):

A. An overall material balance, input = output:

$$F \text{ (feed)} = W \text{ (bottoms)} + D \text{ (distillate)}$$

Since $F = 40$ and $D = 5$, $W = 35$.

B. A material balance for hexane: Let x_D = mole fraction of hexane in D, and x_W = the mole fraction of hexane in W.

$$y_F F = 5x_D + 35x_W = (40)(0.2) = 5(0.9) + 35(x_W)$$
$$x_W = 0.1$$

C. An over-all enthalpy balance: Let

$$Q_C = \text{heat removed in condenser, Btu}$$
$$h = \text{liquid enthalpy, Btu/lb mole}$$
$$H = \text{vapor enthalpy, Btu/lb mole}$$
$$FH_F = Dh_D + Wh_W + Q_C$$

These are all known quantities, provided the thermal conditions of the distillate, feed and bottoms are specified.

D. Plate-to-plate calculations: For the top plate we write
(a) a material balance for hexane

$$y_{n-1}V_{n-1} + L_R x_R = V_n y_n + L_n x_n \qquad (4\text{--}8)$$

(b) an equilibrium relationship. Fig. 2–3 can be considered as an equation of the form $y = f(x)$; so let us call it Eq. 4–9:

$$(\text{Fig. 2–3, on page 17}) \qquad (4\text{--}9)$$

and (c) an enthalpy balance

$$H_{n-1}V_{n-1} = H_n V_n + h_n L_n + Q_C \qquad (4\text{--}10)$$

The known quantities in Eqs. 4–8, 4–9, and 4–10 are Q_C, x_D, L_R, y_n (since $y_n = x_D$), h_D, H_n, and V_n. We are assuming that for a saturated stream the enthalpy is known if the composition is known; thus, the unknowns are y_{n-1}, V_{n-1}, L_n, x_n and H_{n-1}. However, H_{n-1} is known if y_{n-1} is known, and y_n and x_n are not independent variables, being connected by Eq. 4–9. Hence the simultaneous solution of the three equations gives the conditions on plate $n - 1$, and by developing heat and material balances analogous to Eqs. 4–8, 4–9, and 4–10 about plate $n - 1$, we can ascertain the composition on plate $n - 2$. We continue doing this until we reach a plate on which $x_W < 0.1$, the desired bottoms product composition.

Both the analytical and the (yet-to-be-discussed) graphical solutions are greatly simplified if $L_R = L_n = L = \text{constant}$, and $V_n = V_{n-1} = V = \text{constant}$. In this case, we may dispense with one equation, namely, the heat balance. This assumption of constant L/V, *constant molal overflow*, which was also embodied in Eq. 4–6, is valid if:

1. The molar heats of vaporization of all mixtures of the binary system are equal. Then every mole of condensing vapor vaporizes exactly 1 mole of liquid. Since it is the molar latent heats that are presumed to be equal, the flows must be specified in terms of moles, and the concentrations in terms of mole fractions.

2. The heats of mixing, heat losses, and sensible heat changes due to temperature gradients are negligible. Thus, if we consider stage $n - 1$ to be at t_{n-1} and stages n and $n - 2$ to be at t_n and t_{n-2}, the enthalpy balance about stage $n - 1$ can be written to include all enthalpy terms:

(Latent heat in vapor V_{n-2}) + (sensible heat in vapor V_{n-2}, above t_{n-1}) + (heat of mixing) − (sensible heat of liquid L_n, below t_{n-1}) + (latent heat in vapor V_{n-1}) − (heat losses) = 0

(Heat outputs are +, and inputs −.)

The assumption of constant L/V implies that the second, third, fourth, and sixth terms are negligible.

Although in many instances the assumption of constant phase ratio causes no significant error, it is important to understand how deviations from ideal conditions arise:

1. The molal heat of vaporization generally increases with increasing molecular weight. This causes a *net flow* increase up the column, net flow being defined as the difference in the rate of vapor and liquid flow.

2. The temperature decreases up the column. Hence the vapor will be cooled, generally by increased vaporization. This effect results in a net flow increase up the column.

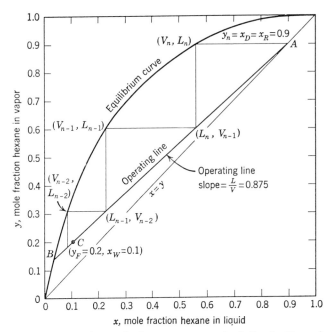

FIG. 4–4. x-y Diagram for hexane-octane and solution for Example 4–1.

3. The liquid flowing down is heated, and this results in a decrease in the net flow up.

It is apparent that these effects are determined largely by the difference in vapor and liquid phase flows and are somewhat compensating when the phase flows are nearly equal.

EXAMPLE 4–1. Using graphical (McCabe-Thiele) methods, calculate the number of stages required to make the separation described in section 4–2 and Fig. 4–3. Assume constant molal overflow.

Solution: A logical start is at point A, $y_n = x_D = x_R = 0.9$. This point is on the $x = y$, line of Fig. 4–4, the McCabe-Thiele diagram for this problem. Since x_R and y_n are passing streams, point A must lie on the operating line, as defined by Eq. 4–6.

$$y_{n-1} = \frac{L}{V} x_n + \frac{V y_n - L x_0}{V} = \frac{L}{V} x_n + \frac{D x_D}{V} \qquad (4\text{–}6a)$$

Here y_{n-1} and x_n are any pair of passing streams and L/V is the slope of the operating line; 0.875, in this case. The line $\overline{ACB}$ is the

Graphical Design Methods—McCabe-Thiele | *71*

operating line for $L/V = 0.875$. It passes through the points $y_n = x_D = 0.9$, and $(x_W = 0.1, y_F = 0.2)$, point C.

We now proceed to work our way down the column by going from the passing streams (L_R, V_n) to the equilibrium streams leaving plate n, (V_n, L_n) to the passing streams below n, (L_n, V_{n-1}), etc. The number of plates required to reach $x_W = 0.1$ is seen to be less than three.

The type of contactor discussed in Example 4–1 is an *enriching column* since its main function is to purify the lower boiling constituent, hexane.

The device is incapable of producing a very pure octane bottoms product because, even if the column had an infinite number of stages, the bottoms composition would contain 4% hexane (point B, Fig. 4–4). In order to produce a higher concentration octane bottoms, plates below the feed point are required—the so-called *stripping section*.

Methods for designing columns having both stripping and enriching sections will be presented in section 4–5.

4–3 APPLICATION TO EXTRACTION

Extraction and absorption introduce an added complexity, since the material balance must take cognizance of three components. In extraction, a solvent S is used to extract a solute from a matrix W. We denote the solvent rich extract phase flow rate by E and the raffinate phase flow by R (Fig. 4–5).

The nomenclature adopted in Fig. 4–5 is:

E_a, E_{n-2}, etc. = Total mass rate in extract phase (at the point specified by the subscript)

E_S = Mass rate of solvent in extract phase (to be assumed constant)

y_a, y_{n-2}, etc. = Mass fraction solute in phase E.

Y_a, Y_{n-2}, etc. = Mass flow solute/mass flow solvent in phase E

R_n, R_{n-1}, etc. = Total mass flow of raffinate phase

R_W = Mass flow of inerts in raffinate phase (to be assumed constant)

x_n, x_{n-1}, etc. = Mass fraction solute in phase R

X_n, X_{n-1}, etc. = Mass flow of solute/mass flow of inerts in phase R

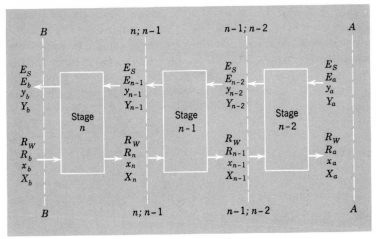

FIG. 4–5. Countercurrent solvent extraction process (schematic).

The overall and component mass balances per unit time are

$$E_a + R_b = E_b + R_a$$

$$R_b x_b + E_a y_a = E_b y_b + R_a x_a$$

or, in terms of mass ratios, if R_W and E_S are constant,

$$R_W(X_b - X_a) = E_S(Y_b - Y_a) \qquad (4\text{–}11)$$

Equation 4–11 is analogous to 4–7 and gives the slope of an operating line in terms of the difference in composition of two passing streams in the column.

$$\frac{R_W}{E_S} = \frac{Y_b - Y_a}{X_b - X_a} = \frac{\Delta Y}{\Delta X} \qquad (4\text{–}12)$$

By similar techniques, taking a mass balance about A and $(n - 1; n - 2)$, we derive an equation analogous to 4–6:

$$E_S Y_a + R_W X_{n-1} = E_S Y_{n-2} + R_W X_a$$

$$Y_{n-2} = \frac{R_W}{E_S}(X_{n-1}) + \frac{E_S Y_a - R_W X_a}{E_S} \qquad (4\text{–}13)$$

Graphical Design Methods—McCabe-Thiele | 73

This gives the relationships of the passing streams between stages $n - 1$ and $n - 2$.

Equation 4–13 is a *straight* operating line for all passing streams between each stage, if the ratio of R_W to E_S is constant from stage to stage. This situation is analogous to the distillation, where a constant mole ratio of liquid to vapor was assumed to exist from stage to stage. Note, however, that the simplifying assumption of constant R_W/E_S permits us to use either mole or mass ratios. Characteristic of the system, which permits the assumption of a constant phase R_W/E_S with a relatively small error, is complete immiscibility or a constant partial miscibility of the raffinate and extract phases.

If the equilibrium curve and the material balance equations are expressed in other than the mass ratio concentrations, X and Y, and mass of solvent and mass of unextracted raffinate, E_S and R_W, the operating line will not be straight, even under conditions of complete immiscibility, since the ratio of total phases is not constant because of the transfer of solute from phase to phase.

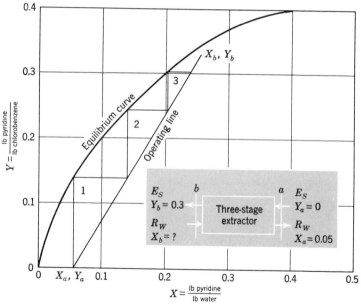

FIG. 4–6. Flow sheet and solution for Example 4–2.

EXAMPLE 4–2.   Pyridine may be removed from water by extraction with chlorobenzene, the equilibrium data being given for the system in Fig. 4–6.

An extract solution containing 0.3 lb pyridine/lb chlorobenzene is to be produced by contacting aqueous pyridine with pure chlorobenzene in a three-stage, countercurrent column. Pyridine concentration in the outlet stream should be not more than 0.05 lb pyridine/lb water.

Assuming that the two phases are mutually insoluble, what is the ratio of feed per pure solvent to be used, and what is the concentration of pyridine in the incoming water layer?

Solution: Basis: 100 lb of feed.

The point $Y_a = 0$, $X_a = 0.05$ is plotted. The point $Y_b = 0.3$, $X_b = 0.235$ is then located by a trial and error procedure, since there is only one operating line which will result in there being three stages between the point X_a, Y_a and the line $Y_b = 0.3$.

The slope of the operating line, R_W/E_S, is 1.6. Thus, on a basis of 100 lb of feed, since $X_B = 0.235$ lb pyridene/lb water, there are 80.9 lb of H_2O in the feed, and 50.6 lb of solvent must be used.

4–4   APPLICATION TO OTHER THREE-COMPONENT SYSTEMS

A. Absorption.   Gas absorption and liquid-liquid extraction are analogous in that in each case we have two carrier streams and a solute which is partitioned between them. The following example illustrates the application of the simplified McCabe-Thiele graphical method to a gas absorption (drying) problem.[1]

EXAMPLE 4–3.   In Fig. 4–7, curve *ABC* gives the equilibrium relationship between moist air and sulfuric acid. Air enters a countercurrent drier with a moisture content $Y_b = 0.028$ moles water/mole dry air, and leaves with a water content $Y_a = 0.008$. The entering acid has a composition of $X_a = 2$ moles water/mole H_2SO_4, and leaves at $X_b = 9$.

(*a*) What is the ratio of liquid absorbent to gas treated?

(*b*) What is the smallest ratio of acid to air which can be employed to dry the air from Y_b to Y_a?

Solution: (*a*) The slope of the operating line *E-F* is the ratio of acid to air treated, 0.00286 mole H_2SO_4/mole dry air.

[1] Walker, Lewis, McAdam, and Gilliland, *Principles of Chemical Engineering*, McGraw-Hill Book Co., New York, 1927.

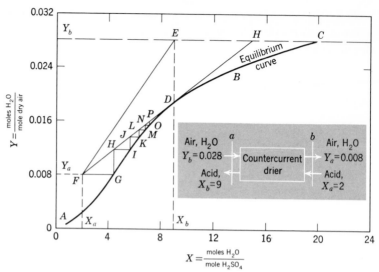

FIG. 4–7. Flow sheet and solution for Example 4–3.

(b) Line F-H is the line of lowest slope through F that can reach $Y_b = 0.028$. It is tangent to the equilibrium line at D and has a slope $= 0.00164$ mole acid/mole air. This is the smallest amount of acid which can be employed, and would result in an inoperable absorber, requiring an infinite number of stages. The "pinch point," D, prevents us from reaching H via $FGHIJKL \ldots$.

B. Ion Exchange. By proper choice of coordinate system, McCabe-Thiele diagrams can be applied to exchange of ion G, in an ion exchange resin, with ion A in solution.

$$A + G \cdot \text{resin} \leftrightharpoons G + A \cdot \text{resin}$$

If y and x are used to denote the ionic fraction on the resin, and in solution, respectively, and the distribution coefficient is $\alpha = (y_A/x_A)/(y_G/x_G) = 3.00$, then the equilibrium data can be presented graphically, as in Fig. 4–8.

Let us assume that the ionic concentration of component A in the solution entering at the top of the continuous countercurrent exchanger of Fig. 4–8 is 1, and that the y_A leaving is 0.7. At the bottom of the exchanger $y_A = 0$, and $x_A = 0.035$.

(a) How many equivalent stages are in the column?

(b) Assuming an equimolal exchange process, and given the following process variables, how many cubic ft per minute of solution can the column process?

ρ = density of resin = 0.65 g/cc (true volume)
Q = total capacity = 5 meq/g (dry)
R = resin flow rate = 10 cu ft/min (true volume)
C = total ionic level in solution = 1 meq/cc
L = solution flow rate, cu ft/min

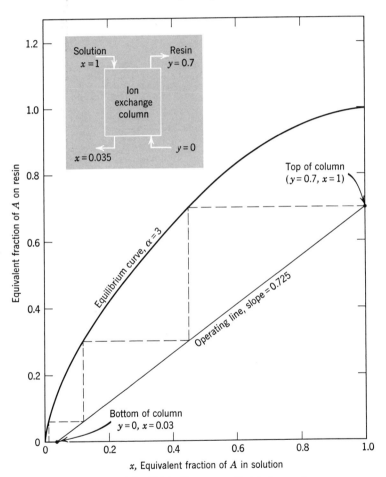

FIG. 4–8. McCabe-Thiele diagram applied to ion exchange.

On a basis of 1 minute:

(*a*) The two passing streams at the end of the column are shown in Fig. 4–8, as is the operating line. It is seen that less than three stages are required.

(*b*) The slope of the operating line is 0.725, and the material balance is:

$$(C)(\Delta x)(L) = (Q)(\rho)(R)(\Delta y)$$

or

$$\frac{\Delta y}{\Delta x} = 0.725 = \frac{CL}{Q\rho R} = \frac{(1)(L)}{(5)(0.65)(10)}$$

$$L = 23.45 \text{ cu ft/min}$$

4–5 DETAILED McCABE-THIELE PROCEDURES—BINARY DISTILLATION

Once the principle of the operating line and the method of stepping off stages are clearly understood, the procedures can be applied to

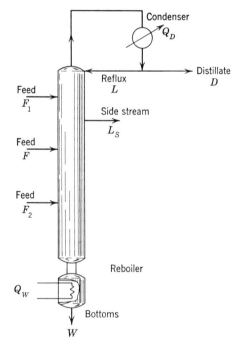

FIG. 4–9. Various distillation operations.

more complex situations. In the case of distillation this might include:

1. Feeding the column at some intermediate plate, while simultaneously returning reflux to the top of the column (Fig. 4–9). The thermal condition of the feed may be a liquid below its boiling point, a saturated liquid, part liquid-part vapor, saturated vapor, or superheated vapor.

2. A multiple feeding arrangement with feeds entering intermediate plates (feeds F_1 and F_2 in Fig. 4–9).

3. Operation at the minimum reflux ratio. As we shall see, this results in a maximum amount of product per unit heat input.

4. Operation at total reflux ($L/V = 1$). This gives the minimum number of plates required to achieve a separation when no feed enters and no product is withdrawn.

5. Withdrawal of an intermediate side stream as a product, as shown in Fig. 4–9.

The column in Fig. 4–10 contains both an enriching section (above the feed) and a stripping section (below the feed). In section 4–2 we developed the operating line for the enriching section (Eq. 4–6); we now proceed to do the same for the stripping section, again at constant L/V. Letting $\bar{V}$ and $\bar{L}$ denote liquid and vapor flows in the stripping section streams and taking a balance about the lower dotted section of the fractionation column in Fig. 4–10, we proceed to make the following:

Overall balance: $\qquad V_m + W = L_{m-1}$ $\qquad\qquad$ (4–14)

Component balance: $y_m V_m + W x_W = L_{m-1} x_{m-1}$

$$y_m = \frac{L_{m-1}}{V_m} x_{m-1} - \frac{W x_W}{V_m} \qquad (4\text{–}15)$$

Enthalpy balance: $\qquad H_m V_m + h_W W = h_{m-1} L_{m-1} + W q_W$

$$\text{where } W q_W = Q_W \qquad (4\text{–}16)$$

The intersection of the stripping section operating line, Eq. (4–15), with the $x = y$ line can be determined by simultaneous solution of $x = y$ and a generalized Eq. 4–15,

$$y\bar{V} + W x_W = \bar{L} x$$

since $\qquad\qquad\qquad \bar{L} - \bar{V} = W$

the intersection is at $\qquad\qquad x = x_W \qquad\qquad (4\text{–}17)$

Just as the intersection of the enriching section operating line with the $x = y$ line occurs at $y = x = x_D$, the intersection of the stripping section line occurs at the composition of the bottoms, x_W.

The locus of the intersections of the enriching section and the stripping section operating lines of Fig. 4–11 is established from

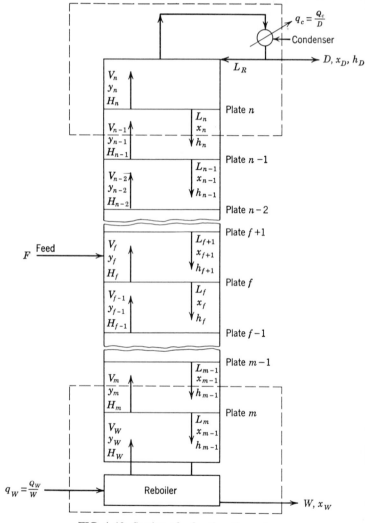

FIG. 4–10. Section of a fractionation column.

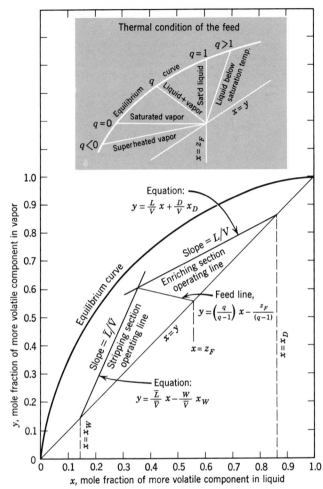

FIG. 4–11. Operating lines on a x-y diagram.

the generalized enriching section operating line, Eq. 4–18, and the generalized stripping section operating line, Eq. 4–19:

$$y = x \frac{L}{V} + \frac{D}{V} x_D \qquad (4\text{–}18)$$

$$y = x \frac{\overline{L}}{\overline{V}} - \frac{W}{\overline{V}} x_W \qquad (4\text{–}19)$$

Graphical Design Methods—McCabe-Thiele | 81

Subtracting:

$$y(V - \bar{V}) = x(L - \bar{L}) + (Dx_D + Wx_W) \qquad (4\text{--}20)$$

We now substitute for the last bracketed term in Eq. 4–20 the overall material balance for Fig. 4–10

$$Fz_F = Dx_D + Wx_W \qquad (4\text{--}21)$$

and for $(V - \bar{V})$ we substitute

$$(V - \bar{V}) = F - (\bar{L} - L)$$

We then obtain:

$$y = \left(\frac{q}{q-1}\right)x - \left(\frac{z_F}{q-1}\right) \qquad (4\text{--}22)$$

where

$$q = \frac{\bar{L} - L}{F} \qquad (4\text{--}23)$$

Equation 4–22 is the equation of a straight line, the so-called q *line*, of slope $\left(\dfrac{q}{q-1}\right)$ which marks the intersection of the two operating lines and intersects the $x = y$ line at $x = z_F$. This permits locating the feed line in Fig. 4–11.

4-6 THERMAL CONDITION OF THE FEED

The magnitude of q is determined by the thermal condition of the feed. This is shown by an energy balance around the feed plate in Fig. 4–10.

$$H_F F + H_{f-1}V_{f-1} + h_{f+1}L_{f+1} = h_f L_f + H_f V_f \qquad (4\text{--}24)$$

Solving Eq. 4–24 simultaneously with a material balance about the feed plate,

$$F + L_{f+1} + V_{f-1} = L_f + V_f \qquad (4\text{--}25)$$

and making the usual simplifying assumptions about constant molar phase ratio, and substituting our definition of q, Eq. 4–23:

$$q = \frac{H_f - H_F}{H_f - h_f} \qquad (4\text{--}26)$$

Equation 4–26 states that the value of q can be established by dividing the enthalpy required to bring the feed to saturated vapor by the latent heat of vaporization. The effect of the thermal condition of the feed on the slope of the q line described by Eq. 4–26 is summarized and shown schematically in the insert of Fig. 4–11.

4–7 DETERMINATION OF THE NUMBER OF THEORETICAL STAGES—REBOILER AND PARTIAL CONDENSER

After the operating lines of the enriching section and the stripping section have been established, the theoretical stages are determined by stepping off plates in accordance with the procedure described in section 4–1.

If the distillation column is equipped with a reboiler, this is equivalent to a single theoretical contact since, in effect, the reboiler accepts a liquid feed stream and discharges liquid and vapor streams in equilibrium, V_W and W in Fig. 4–10. If the overhead vapor is only partially condensed in a *partial condenser*, rather than being totally condensed, this adds another stage to the column. In Fig. 4–12 the streams V^* and L^* are in equilibrium.

4–8 LOCATION OF THE FEED PLATE

The *optimum feed plate location* is at the change-over point from stepping off plates between the enriching section operating line and the equilibrium curve, to stepping off plates between the stripping section operating line and the equilibrium curve (plate 3 in (*a*) of Fig. 4–13). If a feed location below the optimum plate is chosen (plate 5 in (*b*) of Fig. 4–13), it will require more equilibrium contacts to effect the separation. Point K represents the limit of the location of the feed plate below the optimum point. It is impossible to accomplish the required separation of z_F to x_W and x_D at the established reflux ratio below K; K is a *pinch point*, since an infinite number of plates above the feed plate are required to reach K.

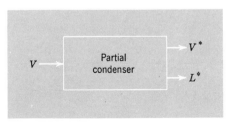

FIG. 4–12. A partial condenser.

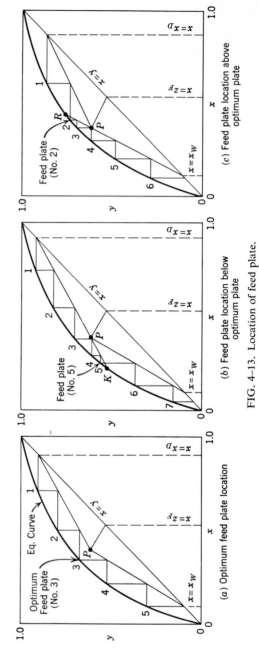

FIG. 4-13. Location of feed plate.

(a) Optimum feed plate location

(b) Feed plate location below optimum plate

(c) Feed plate location above optimum plate

If a feed plate location above the optimum feed plate is chosen as shown in (c) of Fig. 4–13, more equilibrium contacts will be required to effect the separation than if the optimum point were used. In (c) of Fig. 4–13, the second plate from the top was chosen as the feed plate. Point R represents the limit of the location above the optimum plate to accomplish the required separation at the specified reflux ratio.

4-9 LIMITING OPERATING CONDITIONS

(a) *Minimum Number of Plates.* In the enriching section, the steepest slope that any operating line through point x_D can have is $L/V = 1$. Under these conditions there is no product and the number of stages is a minimum for any given separation. For the stripping section, the lowest slope an operating line through x_W can have is $\bar{L}/\bar{V} = 1$, in which case no bottoms stream is withdrawn.

At $L = V$, and with no products, the operating line equations 4–18 and 4–19 become simply $y = x$. This situation, termed *total reflux*, affords the greatest possible area between the equilibrium curve and the operating lines, thus specifying the minimum number of equilibrium stages required to produce x_W and x_D. This condition is shown in Fig. 4–14.

(b) *Minimum Reflux Ratio (L/D or L/V).* Algebraically, $L/D = (L/V)/(1 - L/V)$. The relationship between the two reflux ratios is

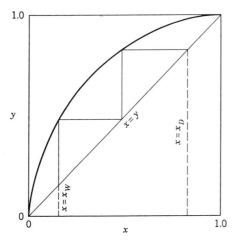

FIG. 4–14. Minimum stages, total reflux.

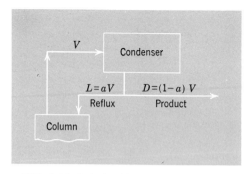

FIG. 4–15. Relationship between L_V and L_0.

best worked out by making a sketch such as Fig. 4–15. Note that L/D is a minimum when L/V is a minimum. Since no point on the operating line can lie above the equilibrium curve, the minimum slope of the operating line is determined by an intersection of an operating line with the equilibrium curve. The two minimum reflux situations which normally occur are shown in Fig. 4–16.

1. The intersection of the two operating lines is seen to fall on the equilibrium curve, (a) in Fig. 4–16.

2. The slope of the enriching section operating line is tangent to the equilibrium lines at point R in (b) of Fig. 4–16.

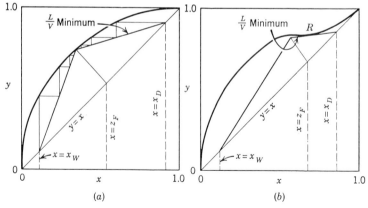

FIG. 4–16. Limiting operating conditions, minimum reflux ratio. (a) Intersection of operating lines at equilibrium curve. (b) Operating line tangent to equilibrium curve.

In either case, an infinite number of stages are required to accomplish the separation. The minimum reflux ratio condition thus corresponds to the situation of maximum product-maximum stages. It is the exact converse of the minimum plate-total reflux-minimum product case.

4–10 STAGE EFFICIENCIES

In previous discussions of stage contacts, it was assumed that the phases leaving the stage were in thermodynamic equilibrium. In actual countercurrent multi-stage equipment, it is not practical to provide the combination of residence time and intimacy of contact required to accomplish equilibrium. Hence, the concentration change for a given stage is less than that predicted by equilibrium considerations.

Stage efficiencies are employed to characterize this condition. The efficiency term often employed is *over-all stage efficiency*.

$$\text{Over-all stage efficiency} = \frac{\text{Theoretical contacts required for given separation} \times 100}{\text{Actual number of contacts required for the same separation.}}$$

This definition has the advantage of being very simple to use; however, it does not take into account the variation in efficiency from one stage in the column to another due to changes in the physical properties of the system caused by changes in composition and temperature.

A stage efficiency frequently used to describe the individual tray performance is termed the *Murphree plate efficiency*. The Murphree plate efficiency can be defined on the basis of either phase and is equal to the change in actual composition of the phase divided by the change predicted by equilibrium considerations. This definition is expressed mathematically as:

$$\text{For the vapor phase: } E_v = \frac{y_n - y_{n-1}}{y_n^* - y_{n-1}} \times 100 \qquad (4\text{--}27)$$

where E_v is the Murphree plate efficiency based on the vapor phase, and y^* is the composition of the hypothetical vapor phase that would be in equilibrium with the liquid composition leaving the actual stage. Similarly, a liquid phase efficiency, E_l, can be defined, using liquid phase concentrations.

Graphical Design Methods—McCabe-Thiele | *87*

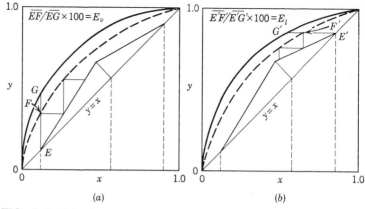

FIG. 4–17. Murphree plate efficiencies. (a) Based on vapor phase, E_v. (b) Based on liquid phase, E_l.

Thus, in stepping off stages, the Murphree plate efficiency dictates the percentage of the distance from the operating line to the equilibrium line taken; it tells us that we should go only E_v or E_l of the total vertical or horizontal path. This is shown in (a) of Fig. 4–17 for the case of Murphree Efficiencies based on the vapor phase, and in Fig. 4–17B for the liquid phase.

4–11 VARIATIONS IN FEED AND PRODUCT OPERATING CONDITIONS

(a) *Multiple Feeds.* A multiple feed arrangement was shown in Fig. 4–9 on page 78. In the absence of side stream L_s this arrangement has no effect on the material balance equations associated with the enriching section of the column above the upper feed point F_1. The section of column between the upper and lower feed points is represented by an operating line of slope L'/V', this line intersecting the enriching section operating line. A similar argument holds for the stripping section of the column. With these considerations in mind, it is possible to apply the McCabe-Thiele graphical principles as shown in Fig. 4–18(a). The operating condition for Fig. 4–9 with $F_1 = F_2 = 0$ but $L_s \neq 0$ is represented graphically in (b) of Fig. 4–18.

For certain types of distillation, instead of the energy being supplied by a reboiler, it is supplied by an inert, hot gas introduced directly into the base of the column. An example of this is the *steam distillation* of fats where the heat is supplied by live steam, no reboiler

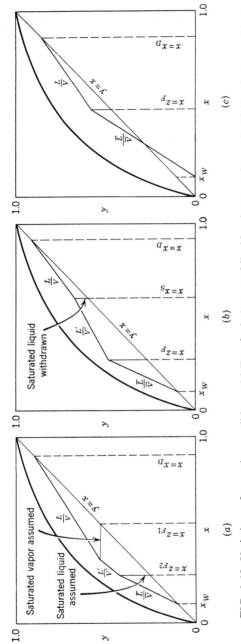

FIG. 4–18. Variations of operating conditions. (a) Two feeds (saturated liquid and saturated vapor). (b) One feed, one side stream (saturated liquid). (c) Open steam system.

Graphical Design Methods—McCabe-Thiele | 89

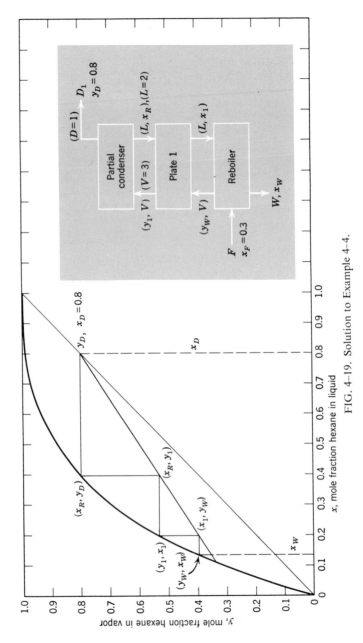

FIG. 4-19. Solution to Example 4-4.

being used. In this case the q_W of Fig. 4–9 is a stream of composition $y = 0$. Thus $y = 0$, $x = x_W$ becomes a point on the operating line, since the passing streams $y = 0$, $x = x_W$ actually exist at the end of the column. The use of open steam rather than a reboiler for the operating condition of $F_1 = F_2 = L_s = 0$ is represented graphically in (c) of Fig. 4–18.

EXAMPLE 4–4. 100 moles per hour of a feed containing 30 mole percent hexane, 70% octane is to be distilled in a column consisting of a still pot, one plate, and a partial condenser. The feed, liquid at its boiling point, is fed to the reboiler, from which a residue is continuously withdrawn. The reflux is returned to the plate. The distillate contains 80 mole percent hexane, and the ratio of liquid reflux flow to distillate flow is 2.

(a) Using McCabe-Thiele procedures, calculate the bottoms composition, and moles of distillate produced per hour.

(b) If the relative volatility, $\alpha = P^\circ$ hexane$/P^\circ$ octane, is assumed constant at 6, do the calculation analytically.

Graphical solution: The diagrams of the still and the L/V, L/D relationships are given in Fig. 4–19, as is the graphical solution which is constructed in the following manner:

Basis: one hour.

1. The point $y_D = x_D = 0.8$ is located on the $x = y$ line.

2. Conditions in the condenser are fixed, because x_R is in equilibrium with y_D, hence the point x_R, y_D is located.

3. The operating line, slope $L/V = 2/3$, is now drawn through the point $y_D = x_D = 0.8$.

4. Three theoretical stages (two plates plus reboiler) are stepped off and the bottoms composition, $x_W = 0.135$, is read.

The amount of distillate is determined from an over-all material balance, since $W = 100 - D$.

$$(0.3)(100) = (0.8)(D) + (0.135)(100 - D)$$
$$D = 24.8$$

Analytical solution: Instead of a diagrammatic representation, we now have an analytical expression for the x-y equilibrium relationship (see Eq. 2–6, section 2–3).

$$x = \frac{y}{y + \alpha(1 - y)} \qquad (4\text{–}28)$$

The steps in the solution are now as follows:

1. The liquid leaving the partial condenser x_R is

$$x_R = \frac{0.8}{0.8 + 6(1 - 0.8)} = 0.4$$

2. y_1 is determined by a material balance about the partial condenser.

$$Vy_1 = Dx_D + Lx_R$$

$$y_1 = (\tfrac{1}{3})(0.8) + (\tfrac{2}{3})(0.4) = 0.534$$

3. $x_1 = \dfrac{0.534}{0.534 + 6(1 - 0.534)} = 0.160$

4. $Vy_W = Dx_D + Lx_1$

$$y_W = \tfrac{1}{3}(0.8) + \tfrac{2}{3}(0.160) = 0.374$$

5. $x_W = \dfrac{0.374}{0.374 + 6(1 - 0.374)} = 0.091$

By approximating the equilibrium data with $\alpha = 6$, an answer of $0.091 = x_W$ rather than $x_W = 0.135$ has been obtained.

EXAMPLE 4–5.   Solve Example 4–4 graphically, assuming the feed is introduced on plate 1, rather than into the still pot.

What would be the minimum number of plates required to carry out the separation?

Solution: The flow sheet and the solution are given in Fig. 4–20*A*. The solution was obtained as follows:

1. The point x_R, y_D is located on the equilibrium line.

2. The operating line for the enriching section is drawn through $y = x = 0.8$; $L/V = \tfrac{2}{3}$.

3. The intersection of the q line, $x_F = 0.3$ (saturated liquid) with the enriching section operating line is located. The stripping section operating line must also go through this point, point P.

4. The stripping section operating line is found by trial and error, there being three equilibrium contacts in the column, two of which lie between P and x_W. $x_W = 0.07$, and the amount of distillate is

$$(0.3)(100) = (0.8D) + 0.07(100 - D)$$

$$D = 31.5$$

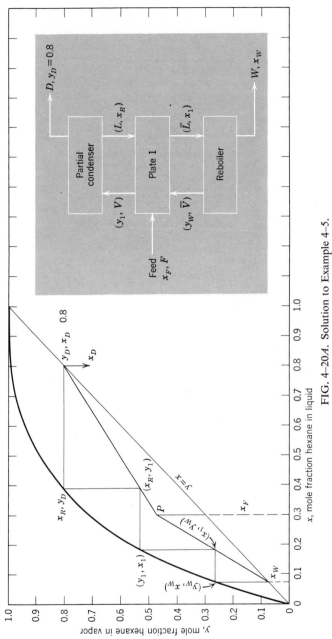

FIG. 4-20A. Solution to Example 4-5.

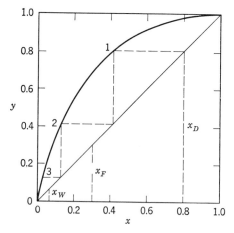

FIG. 4–20B. Solution to total reflux case in Example 4–5.

Note that the operation of the column has been improved by introduction of the feed on plate 1, rather than into the reboiler as was done in Example 4–4.

The construction corresponding to total reflux ($L/V = 1$, no product, minimum plates) is seen in Fig. 4–20B. For this case, slightly more than two stages are required.

EXAMPLE 4–6. A continuous rectifying column, equipped with a reboiler and total condenser and operating on a saturated liquid feed, has a side stream take-off in the enriching section. Making the usual simplifying assumptions:

(a) Derive an equation for the operating lines in the enriching section.

(b) Find the point of intersection of these operating lines.

(c) Find their intersection with the diagonal.

(d) Show the construction on an x-y diagram.

Solution: (a) Taking a material balance over section 1 in Fig. 4–21, we obtain,

$$y_{n-1} = \frac{L}{V} x_n + \frac{D}{V} x_D$$

About section 2,

$$V_{s-2} y_{s-2} = L'_{s-1} x_{s-1} + L_s x_s + D x_D$$

Invoking the usual simplifying assumptions

$$y = \frac{L'}{V} x + \frac{L_s x_s + D x_D}{V} \quad \text{and} \quad y = \frac{L}{V} x + \frac{D}{V} x_D$$

(b) The intersection of the two operating lines occurs at

$$(L - L')x = L_s x_s$$

and, since $L - L' = L_s$, the point of intersection becomes $x = x_s$.

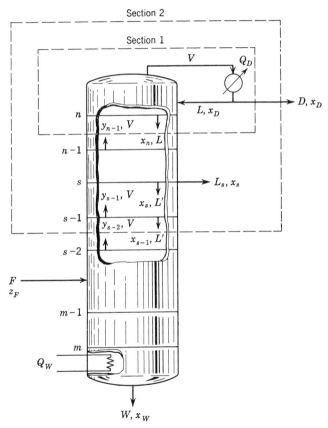

FIG. 4–21. Flow sheet for Example 4–6.

Graphical Design Methods—McCabe-Thiele | 95

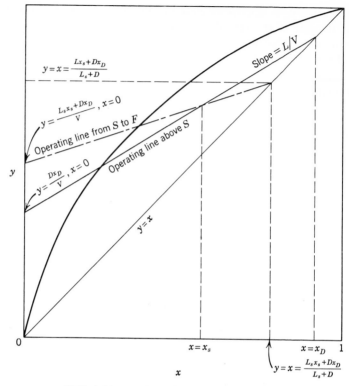

FIG. 4–22. Graphical solution to Example 4–6.

(c) The intersection of the lines

$$y = \frac{L'}{V} x + \frac{L_s x_s + D x_D}{V}$$

and

$$y = x$$

can be shown to occur at

$$x = \frac{L_s x_s + D x_D}{L_s + D}$$

(d) The x-y diagram is shown in Fig. 4–22.

EXAMPLE 4–7.   Derive an equation which can be used to calculate the number of theoretical contacts required to make a given separation when a column operates at total reflux and constant pressure, and the relative volatility, α, may be assumed constant.

Solution: Taking the two consecutive plates $n-1$ and $n-2$, at total reflux,

$$y_{n-2} = x_{n-1} \qquad (4\text{–}29)$$

The equilibrium relationships are

$$\frac{y_{n-1}}{1 - y_{n-1}} = \alpha \frac{x_{n-1}}{1 - x_{n-1}} \qquad (4\text{–}30)$$

and

$$\frac{y_{n-2}}{1 - y_{n-2}} = \alpha \frac{x_{n-2}}{1 - x_{n-2}} \qquad (4\text{–}31)$$

Substituting among Eqs. 4–29, 4–30, and 4–31 yields

$$\frac{y_{n-1}}{1 - y_{n-1}} = \alpha^2 \frac{x_{n-2}}{1 - x_{n-2}} \qquad (4\text{–}32)$$

In the limit, as we go up the column in x, $y_{n-1} \rightarrow y_D = x_D$ and $x_{n-2} \rightarrow x_W$ and $\alpha^2 \rightarrow \alpha^N$, where $N =$ number of stages. Hence,

$$\frac{x_D}{1 - x_D} = \alpha^N \frac{x_W}{1 - x_W}$$

$$N = \frac{\log \dfrac{x_D(1 - x_W)}{x_W(1 - x_D)}}{\log \alpha} \qquad (4\text{–}33)$$

Equation 4–33 is known as the Fenske equation.[1]

4–12   APPLICATION OF McCABE-THIELE METHODS TO OTHER OPERATIONS

Adaption of the basic McCabe-Thiele methods to other processes is not difficult, *provided* the equilibrium data for the system can be shown on an x-y type diagram in such a fashion that the slope represents the ratio of the two phases.

Example 4–8 illustrates the application of the McCabe-Thiele graphical method to absorption.

[1] *Ind. Eng. Chem.*, **24**, 482 (1932).

EXAMPLE 4–8.   A mixture of air and acetone vapor, containing 85 volume percent air, is to be "stripped" of 95 % of its acetone content by countercurrent contact with a stream of water in a bubble plate column.   The column operates at 68°F and 1 atmosphere pressure. An over-all plate efficiency of 30 % is expected.   Equilibrium data for acetone-water at 20°C are:

Mole percent acetone in
liquid   3.33   7.20   11.7   17.1

Acetone partial pressure,
mm Hg   30.0   62.8   85.4   103.0

Using the above data, calculate:

(*a*) Minimum value of L/G, the ratio of moles of water per mole of air.

(*b*) The number of actual plates required, using a value of L/G of 1.25 times the minimum.

(*c*) The concentration of acetone in the exit water.

Solution: Assumptions: (1) no water vaporized; (2) no acetone in entering water; (3) no air dissolves in the water.   Basis: 100 moles of entering gas.

Column bottom:

$$\begin{array}{ll}
\text{Acetone in gas} & \text{15 moles} \\
\text{Air in gas} & \text{85 moles}
\end{array}$$

$Y_B = 15/85 = 0.176$ mole acetone/mole air

Column top:

$$\begin{array}{ll}
\text{Acetone in gas } (0.05)(15) & \text{0.75 mole} \\
\text{Air in gas} & \text{85.00 moles}
\end{array}$$

$Y_T = 0.75/85 = 0.00882$ mole acetone/mole air

EQUILIBRIUM CURVE DATA: (P = 760 mm Hg)

x	$1-x$	X $x/(1-x)$	y (p/P)	$1-y$	Y $y/(1-y)$
0		0	0		0
0.033	0.967	0.0341	0.0395	0.9605	0.0411
0.072	0.928	0.0776	0.0827	0.9173	0.0901
0.117	0.883	0.1327	0.1122	0.8873	0.1265
0.171	0.829	0.2065	0.1258	0.8642	0.1572

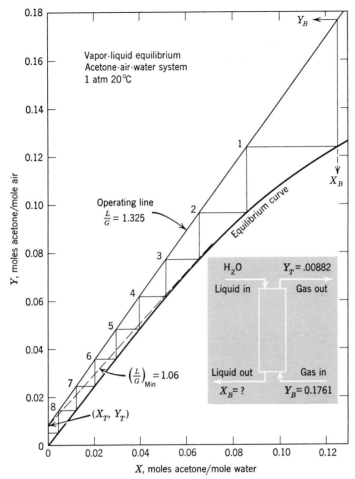

FIG. 4–23. Solution to Example 4–8.

These data are now plotted in Fig. 4–23 as X versus Y, since these coordinates linearize the operating line.

(a) Minimum solvent rate:

  Tangent to curve from point $X_T = 0$, $Y_T = 0.00882$
  $(L/G)_{Min} = 1.06$ moles H_2O/mole air (see graph)

(b) Actual plates required:

  $L/G = 1.25(L/G)_{Min} = 1.325$ moles H_2O/mole air

Intersection of the operating line with $Y_B = 0.176$ occurs at $X_B = 0.126$.

$$\text{Theoretical plates} = 8.5$$
$$\text{Actual plates} = \text{t.p.}/0.30 = 28.3 = 29$$

4-13 COST CONSIDERATIONS

For the stage contact problems considered, a solution was obtained for given operating conditions, reflux ratio, number of plates, feed location, etc. There are an infinite number of possible solutions for a given separation requirement. The final decision is based primarily on cost considerations. These costs include capital costs for the equipment and installation and operating costs of utilities, labor, raw materials, and maintenance.

Increased reflux ratio, for example, has the effect of decreasing the required number of theoretical contacts, but it increases the equipment diameter and steam requirements. It is frequently necessary to solve the separation problem a considerable number of times, imposing various operating conditions and carefully ascertaining the effect on the total cost of the particular solution proposed.

Further discussions of optimum design procedures are considered in Chapter 10.

five | batch operations

In batch operations, an initial quantity of material is charged to the equipment and, during the operation, one or more phases are continuously withdrawn. A familiar example is the ordinary laboratory distillation. Liquid is charged to a distillation flask, heated to boiling, and the vapor formed is continuously removed and condensed.

One feature of the batch separation is that the composition of the initial charge changes with time during the course of the separation. In batch distillation, for example, when samples of liquid are continuously withdrawn and analyzed, a decrease in the relative amount of the lower boiling components is expected as the distillation proceeds.

Batch operation is used to advantage if:

1. The required operating capacity of a proposed facility is too small to permit continuous operation at a practical rate. Pumps, piping, instrumentation, and other auxiliary equipment generally have a minimum industrial operating capacity.

2. The operating requirements of a facility fluctuate widely in characteristics of feed material as well as processing rate. Batch equipment usually has considerably more operating flexibility than continuous equipment. This is the reason for the predominance of batch equipment provided for multi-purpose solvent recovery or pilot plant applications in the chemical industry.

5-1 DIFFERENTIAL DISTILLATIONS

Consider a batch still with a finite liquid holdup, L, from which a differential amount of vapor, V, is withdrawn at any time. The vapor is withdrawn as soon as it is formed, so there is no vapor phase. The material balance is

$$d(yV) = -d(Lx) \tag{5–1}$$

$$V\,dy + y\,dV = -L\,dx - x\,dL$$

For a differential distillation, $dV = -dL$, and $V\,dy \cong 0$; hence we obtain the Rayleigh equation,

$$\int \frac{dL}{L} = \int \frac{dx}{y - x} \tag{5–2}$$

where the y and x are in equilibrium. Solutions for the case of $y = Kx$ and $\alpha = $ constant are available.[1]

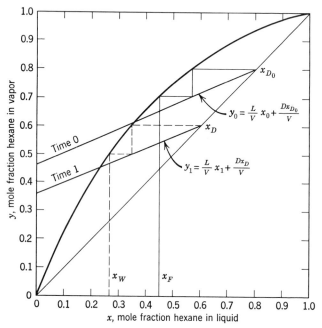

FIG. 5–1. Batch distillation with reflux.

[1] Perry, *Chemical Engineers' Handbook*, McGraw-Hill Book Co.

5-2 BATCH DISTILLATION WITH REFLUX

A batch column with an initial reboiler loading functions as an enriching section. If the reflux ratio be fixed and the column has a fixed number of plates, the distillate and still bottoms composition will vary with time.

Initially, at the beginning of the distillation, the composition of the liquid in the reboiler of the column in Fig. 5-1 is the feed composition x_F. If there are two stages the initial distillate composition x_{D_o} is found by trial and error, if L/V is fixed. At an arbitrary time t, at still pot composition x_W, the distillate composition is x_D. A time-dependent series of points is thus established by trial and error, L/V and the stages being fixed.

It is important to note that Eq. 5-2 cannot be integrated directly if the column has more than one stage, because the relationship between x and y is not an equilibrium relationship such as $y = Kx$, but the compositions of y's and x's in the still pot and distillate.

EXAMPLE 5-1. A three-stage batch column is charged with 100 moles of a 20 mole percent hexane in octane mix. At an L/V ratio of 0.5, how much material must be distilled if an average product composition of 70 mole percent C_6 is required?

Solution: A series of operating lines and hence x_W's are obtained by a trial procedure which consists of fitting three stages onto an operating line of slope $L/V = 0.5$ anchored initially at $x_F = 0.2$ (Fig. 5-2). It is then possible to construct Table 5-1, noting that the y and x of Eq. 5-2 are $y = y_D = x_D$, and $x = x_W$.

TABLE 5-1

GRAPHICAL INTEGRATION, EXAMPLE 5-1

y_D	x_W	$\dfrac{1}{y - x}$
0.85	0.2	1.54
0.60	0.09	1.98
0.5	0.07	2.32
0.35	0.05	3.33
0.3	0.035	3.77

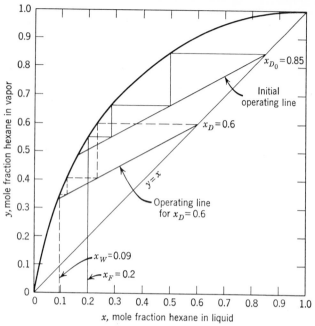

FIG. 5-2. Solution to Example 5-1.

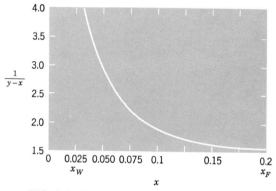

FIG. 5-3. Graphical integration, Example 5-1.

The graphical integration is shown in Fig. 5–3. At $x_W = 0.1$, for instance,

$$\ln \frac{100}{W} = \int_{0.1}^{0.2} \frac{dx}{y - x} = 0.162$$

Hence $W = 85$, $D = 15$

$$(x_D)_{\text{avg}} = \frac{(100)(0.20) - (85)(0.1)}{15} = 0.77$$

The $(x_D)_{\text{avg}}$ is too high; hence, another x_W must be chosen. By trial, the correct answer is found to be $x_W = 0.06$, $D = 22$, $W = 78$.

six / flash distillation

Not all mixtures need to be distilled in fractionation units. In many applications, particularly those involving petroleum processing, only gross separations need be made, and so-called flash distillations can be used.

Figure 6–1 depicts a flash still. A volatile feed is pumped into a heater (pipe still) through a pressure-reducing valve, and into a flash-disengaging chamber. The vapor and liquid leaving the chamber are presumed to be in equilibrium. Let z be the fraction of feed converted to vapor, V/F. On a 1-mole-of-feed basis, a balance for the more volatile component yields

$$x_F = zy_D + (1 - z)x_W \tag{6-1}$$

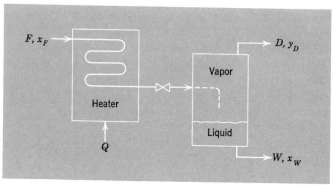

FIG. 6–1. Flash vaporization system.

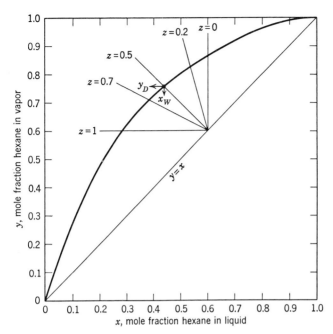

FIG. 6–2. Flash vaporization on x-y diagram.

y_D and x_W are in equilibrium. Generalizing Eq. 6–1,

$$y = -\frac{(1-z)}{z}\,x + \frac{x_F}{z} \qquad (6\text{--}2)$$

Equation 6–2 describes an operating line of slope $-(1-z)/z$ in x-y coordinates. When solved simultaneously with the $y = x$ line, the two lines are seen to intersect at $x = y = x_F$.

A graphical method for obtaining the composition of the exit streams y_D and x_W as a function of z immediately suggests itself. Assume, for instance, that a feed of 60 mole percent hexane-octane is fed to a pipe still. If $z = 0.5$, then $-(1-z)/z = -1$. A line of slope -1 passing through $x = y = 0.6$ intersects the equilibrium curve of Fig. 6–2 at $y_D = 0.75$, $x_W = 0.45$, the compositions of the vapor and liquid leaving the disengager. y_D and x_W values corresponding to other z's are also shown.

seven / the Ponchon Savarit method

McCabe-Thiele constructions, as described in Chapter 4, embody rather restrictive tenets. The assumption of constant molal overflow or mutual insolubility of the phases seriously curtails the general utility of the method. Continued use of McCabe-Thiele procedures can be ascribed to the fact that (*a*) it represents a fairly good engineering approximation, and (*b*) sufficient thermodynamic data to justify a more accurate approach is often lacking. In the case of distillation, enthalpy concentration data needed for making plate-to-plate heat balances are often unavailable, while in the case of absorption or extraction, complete phase equilibrium data may not be at hand.

7–1 MASS AND ENERGY BALANCES ON ENTHALPY-CONCENTRATION DIAGRAMS

According to the First Law of Thermodynamics, the energy conservation equation per unit mass for a steady state, constant mass flow process is[1]

$$\delta q - \delta W_s = dh + d(U^2/2g_c) + dz$$

If the system is adiabatic, $\delta q = 0$; if no shaft work is done, $\delta W_s = 0$; if the kinetic energy effects are negligible, $d(U^2/2g_c) = 0$; and if the elevation above the datum plane is constant, $dz = 0$. Hence only the enthalpy term remains,

$$dh = 0 \qquad (7-1)$$

[1] For work done by the system, $w = +$; for heat rejected, $q = -$.

We now apply Eq. 7–1 to a mixing process where streams A and B are combined to form C, h_A, h_B, and h_C, being the respective enthalpies per unit mass of the stream designated by the subscript. If A, B, and C denote mass flow rates, then $C = A + B$ and

$$h_A A + h_B B = h_C C = h_C(A + B) \tag{7–2}$$

and

$$x_A A + x_B B = x_C C = x_C(A + B) \tag{7–3}$$

Simultaneous solution of Eqs. 7–2 and 7–3 yields

$$\frac{x_B - x_C}{h_B - h_C} = \frac{x_C - x_A}{h_C - h_A} \tag{7–4}$$

Equation 7–4 is the three-point form of a straight line and is shown in a one-phase field on an h-x diagram in Fig. 7–1.

Both Eq. 7–4 and Fig. 7–1 demonstrate that the point (x_C, h_C) must lie on a straight line connecting the points (x_A, h_A) and (x_B, h_B), since the slopes between point A and C and C and B are equal. As usual, the ratio of line segments represents the weight ratios of the corresponding streams.

In addition to representing the addition process $A + B = C$, the line $\overline{ABC}$ represents the equivalent subtraction, $B = C - A$. This point is brought up only to introduce the concept of B as a *difference point*. It is also useful to recall the geometric relationship between

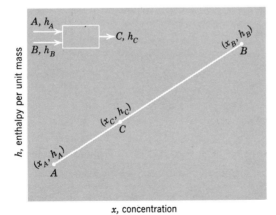

FIG. 7–1. Mixing process on an enthalpy concentration diagram.

two right triangles having parallel sides; namely, that the ratios of all parallel sides are equal. For instance, in Fig. 7–1,

$$\frac{\overline{BC}}{\overline{CA}} = \frac{x_B - x_C}{x_C - x_A} = \frac{h_B - h_C}{h_C - h_A} = \frac{A}{B} \qquad (7\text{–}5)$$

7–2 NON-ADIABATIC MASS AND ENERGY BALANCES

Under non-adiabatic conditions q is not zero, and Eq. 7–1 becomes

$$q = \Delta h$$

For multi-component systems, the q may be defined on the basis of a unit mass of any of the streams. To wit, if Q is total heat transfer, the thermal absorption per unit mass of A and B becomes

$$q_A = \frac{Q}{A}; \qquad q_B = \frac{Q}{B}; \qquad q_C = \frac{Q}{A+B} = \frac{Q}{C}$$

If q_A is factored into Eq. 7–2,

$$(h_A + q_A)A + h_B B = h_C C \qquad (7\text{–}6)$$

Analogously, Eq. 7–4 becomes

$$\frac{x_B - x_C}{h_B - h_C} = \frac{x_C - x_A}{h_C - (h_A + q_A)} \qquad (7\text{–}7)$$

In Fig. 7–2, the graphical representation of Eq. 7–7, the point h_A

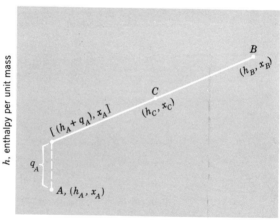

FIG. 7–2. A non-adiabatic mixing process.

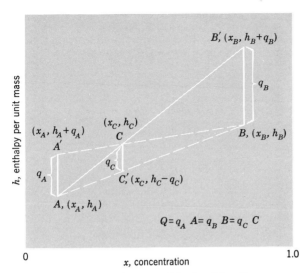

FIG. 7–3. Composite non-adiabatic mixing diagram.

is replaced by $(h_A + q_A)$. Alternatively, if Eq. 7–6 were written in terms of q_B, then the h_B in Eq. 7–7 would be replaced by $(h_B + q_B)$; if it were written in terms of q_C, the h_C would become $(h_C - q_C)$.

Figure 7–3 shows the three equivalent ways of representing the non-adiabatic mixing process. By assigning the entire energy effect to stream A, B, or C, we create, respectively, the virtual streams A', B', or C'. These points must lie on a straight line drawn through the other two actual points; i.e., $\overline{A'CB}$, $\overline{AC'B}$, and $\overline{ACB'}$ must fall on different straight lines.

7–3 COUNTERCURRENT MULTI-STAGE CONTACTS BY ENTHALPY CONCENTRATION (PONCHON-SAVARIT) METHODS

Consider the $n-1$ stage of Fig. 7–4 as a mixing device where streams L_n, V_{n-2} enter, and the equilibrated streams V_{n-1}, L_{n-1} leave. In Fig. 7–5 the mixing-equilibrating action of the plate is shown in two stages. The vapor V_{n-2} and liquid L_n are mixed to form stream z, which then separates into the two equilibrium vapor and liquid phases V_{n-1}, L_{n-1}.

Figure 7–5 demonstrates the basic concept behind the Ponchon-Savarit method. In the McCabe-Thiele construction, material balance equations are plotted on an x-y phase equilibrium diagram,

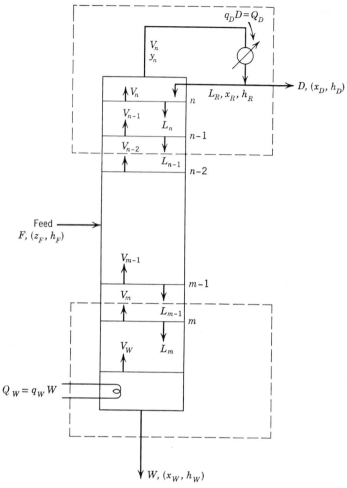

FIG. 7–4. Fractionation column.

the stages being calculated by alternate use of the material balance and equilibrium relationships. In the Ponchon method we are plotting *both* energy and material balance relationships on a phase equilibrium diagram, and thus are in effect making energy balances on each plate. There being no assumptions at all with regard to constant molal overflow, the calculations can be done on a per mole or per pound basis. Any set of consistent units may be used.

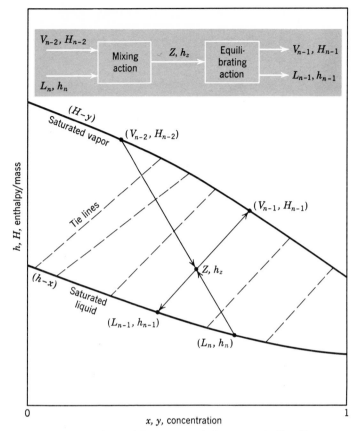

FIG. 7–5. Two-phase mixing on an enthalpy concentration diagram.

The design equations are developed by making material and energy balances about the portion of the enriching section of the column in Fig. 7–4 enclosed within the dotted line. For the more volatile component, the mass balance is

$$y_{n-2}V_{n-2} = x_{n-1}L_{n-1} + Dx_D \qquad (7\text{–}8)$$

the overall balance is

$$V_{n-2} = L_{n-1} + D \qquad (7\text{–}9)$$

and the energy balance is:

$$q_D D + H_{n-2}V_{n-2} = h_{n-1}L_{n-1} + h_D D \qquad (7\text{–}10)$$

The Ponchon Savarit Method | *113*

Solving Eqs. 7–8 and 7–9 simultaneously,

$$\frac{L_{n-1}}{D} = \frac{x_D - y_{n-2}}{y_{n-2} - x_{n-1}} \tag{7-11}$$

while simultaneous solution of Eqs. 7–9 and 7–10 gives:

$$\frac{L_{n-1}}{D} = \frac{(h_D - q_D) - H_{n-2}}{H_{n-2} - h_{n-1}} \tag{7-12}$$

where q_D is heat removed from the stream, and hence negative.

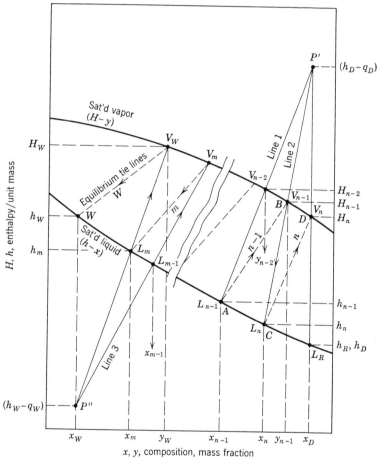

FIG. 7–6. Material balances on an enthalpy concentration diagram.

Combining Eqs. 7–11 and 7–12, we obtain the operating line equation

$$\frac{(h_D - q_D) - H_{n-2}}{x_D - y_{n-2}} = \frac{H_{n-2} - h_{n-1}}{y_{n-2} - x_{n-1}} \qquad (7\text{–}13)$$

Equation 7–13 is an operating line which is the locus of the two passing streams V_{n-2} and L_{n-1}. The equation, which is a three-point equation of a straight line on a Ponchon diagram, states that the points $(h_D - q_D, x_D)$, (H_{n-2}, y_{n-2}), and (h_{n-1}, x_{n-1}) lie on the same straight line, since the slopes between $(h_D - q_D, x_D)$, (H_{n-2}, y_{n-2}), and (H_{n-2}, y_{n-2}), (h_{n-1}, x_{n-1}) are equal, and the two lines have one point (H_{n-2}, y_{n-2}) in common. If all phases are saturated, then the points denoting streams V_{n-1} and L_{n-1} lie on the saturated vapor and liquid lines, respectively. In Fig. 7–6 the line satisfying the conditions of Eq. 7–13 is labeled Line 1.

The point P', whose coordinates are $(h_D - q_D, x_D)$ is called *the difference or net flow point*, since $P' = V_{n-2} - L_{n-1}$.

7–4 IDEAL STAGES ON A PONCHON DIAGRAM

If the lower limit of the material balance loop in the enriching section of the column of Fig. 7–4 had cut the column between plates n and $n - 1$, instead of between $n - 1$ and $n - 2$, an operating line equation equivalent to Eq. 7–13 would be obtained

$$\frac{(h_D - q_D) - H_{n-1}}{x_D - y_{n-1}} = \frac{H_{n-1} - h_n}{y_{n-1} - x_n} \qquad (7\text{–}14)$$

Equation 7–14 is shown as Line 2 on Fig. 7–6. This line also contains the difference point, P'.

To illustrate the method of stepping off plates, consider L_{n-1}, the liquid leaving plate $n - 1$. This stream is to be found on the material balance line $\overline{P'A}$. Since L_{n-1} is in equilibrium with V_{n-1}, we proceed to V_{n-1} along the tie line $n - 1$ (path $\overline{AB}$). V_{n-1} is a passing stream with L_n; hence the next step is from B to C. At C, L_n is in equilibrium with V_n; hence our next step is from C to D.

Note that once we have located the difference point P' *all* passing streams, between any two plates, lie on a line which terminates at point P' and cuts the phase envelope. If the liquid and vapor are saturated, their compositions are determined by the points at which the material balance line cuts the liquid and vapor phase envelopes.

The internal reflux ratios in each stage of the column can be expressed in terms of the line segments and coordinates of Fig. 7–6. The ratio of liquid to vapor between plate $n - 1$ and $n - 2$, for instance, is

$$\frac{L_{n-1}}{V_{n-2}} = \frac{\overline{V_{n-2}P'}}{\overline{L_{n-1}P'}} = \frac{x_D - y_{n-2}}{x_D - x_{n-1}} = \frac{(h_D - q_D) - H_{n-2}}{(h_D - q_D) - h_{n-1}}$$

while the ratio of reflux to distillate on the top plate is

$$\frac{L_R}{D} = \frac{\overline{P'V_n}}{\overline{V_nL_R}} = \frac{(h_D - q_D) - H_n}{H_n - h_R}$$

These relationships apply even if one of the streams is not saturated. L_R, for instance, might be, and usually is, sub-cooled.

Note that the difference point P' may be located if the reflux ratio at the top of the column and the composition and thermal condition of the product are known.

7–5 THE STRIPPING SECTION

The principles developed in sections 7–3 and 7–4 apply to the stripping as well as to the enriching sections of the column in Fig. 7–4.

Simultaneous mass, heat, and component balances about the portion of the column enclosed in the dotted envelope of Fig. 7–6 yield

$$\frac{(h_W - q_W) - H_m}{x_W - y_m} = \frac{H_m - h_{m-1}}{y_m - x_{m-1}} \qquad (7\text{--}15)$$

where q_W is the energy *added* to the reboiler per unit mass of bottoms. Equation 7–15, like 7–13, is an operating line equation because it is the locus of the two passing streams V_m and L_{m-1}. The material balance line defined by Eq. 7–15 is shown as Line 3 in Fig. 7–6. Point P'' is the difference point for the stripping section, the ratio of liquid to vapor between stages m and $m - 1$ being

$$\frac{\overline{L}_{m-1}}{\overline{V}_m} \frac{\overline{P''V_m}}{\overline{P''L_{m-1}}}$$

Stepping off the stages in the stripping section is performed in the same manner as for the enriching section. From L_{m-1} we go to V_m, hence to L_m along tie line m, etc., to the passing stream V_W, and hence to W, the still pot acting as a plate.

As before, we note that all operating lines in the stripping section pass through P'', and that the compositions of any two saturated passing streams are marked by the points where the straight lines through P'' cut the phase envelopes.

7-6   THE OVER-ALL COLUMN

Considering the entire column in Fig. 7–4, we write a composite mass balance

$$F = D + W \tag{7-16}$$

a component balance

$$z_F F = x_D D + x_W W \tag{7-17}$$

and an enthalpy balance

$$F h_F + q_W W + q_D D = h_D D + h_W W \tag{7-18}$$

Algebraic manipulations involving Eqs. 7–16, 7–17, and 7–18 produce a composite balance line passing through (h_F, z_F), and the two difference points, $(h_W - q_W, x_W)$ and $(h_D - q_D, x_D)$.

$$\frac{D}{W} = \frac{h_F - (h_W - q_W)}{z_F - x_W} = \frac{(h_D - q_D) - h_F}{x_D - z_F} \tag{7-19}$$

The line $\overline{P'P''}$ in Fig. 7–7 is a plot of Eq. 7–19. Presented also are other pertinent constructions whose relationships to column parameters are summarized in Table 7–1.

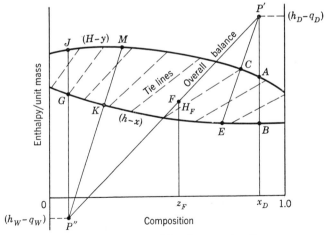

FIG. 7–7. Summary of Ponchon constructions.

EXAMPLE 7–1.   One hundred g moles per hour of saturated hexane-octane vapor containing 69 mole% hexane is separated by distillation at atmospheric pressure into product containing 90 mole% hexane and bottoms containing 5 mole% hexane. The total condenser returns 42.5 mole% of the condensate to the column as

TABLE 7–1

SUMMARY OF PONCHON DIAGRAM CONSTRUCTION IN FIG. 7–7
(All phases assumed saturated)

Section of Column	Line Segments (Fig. 7–7)	Significance
Enriching	$\overline{P'B}$	Heat removed in condenser per pound of distillate
Enriching	$\overline{CP'}/\overline{EP'}$	L/V general
Enriching	$\overline{AP'}/\overline{BP'}$	L/V on top plate (internal reflux ratio)
Enriching	$\overline{AP'}/\overline{AB}$	L/D on top plate (external reflux ratio)
Stripping	$\overline{P''G}$	Heat added in reboiler per pound of bottoms
Stripping	$\overline{MP''}/\overline{KP''}$	$\bar{L}/\bar{V}$ general
Stripping	$\overline{MP''}/\overline{MK}$	$\bar{L}/W$ general
Over-all	$\overline{P'P''}/\overline{FP''}$	F/D
Over-all	$\overline{FP''}/\overline{FP'}$	D/W

saturated liquid.   Using the graphical Ponchon method and the enthalpy-concentration data of Fig. 2–10, calculate:

(a) The rate of production of bottoms and overhead.

(b) The Btu per hour supplied to the boiler and removed at the condenser.

(c) The compositions of streams V_{n-1}, L_n, V_m, and L_{m-1} of Fig. 7–4.

Solution (Basis one hour):   The point F is located on the saturated vapor line at $z_F = 0.69$.   Next we locate P' by virtue of the fact that $L_R/V_n = 0.425$.   On Fig. 7–8, $\overline{P'V_n}/\overline{P'L_R} = 0.425$.

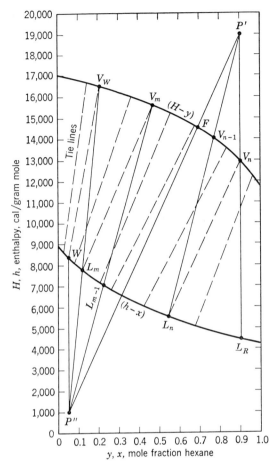

FIG. 7–8. Solution to Example 7–1.

Next, the over-all balance line $\overline{P'FP''}$ is drawn, and the point P'' is located at the intersection of the balance line with $x_W = 0.05$.

(a) $D/F = \overline{FP''}/\overline{P'P''} = 0.75$

$D = 75$ moles/hour

$W = 25$ moles/hour

Check via an over-all hexane balance:

$$100(0.69) = 69 = (0.9)(75) + (0.05)(25) = 68.75$$

(b) $q_D = (19,000 - 4,500)$ cal/g mole of product

$$Q_D = \frac{14,500}{} \left| \frac{\text{cal}}{\text{g mole}} \right| \frac{75 \text{ g mole}}{\text{hr}} \left| \frac{\text{Btu}}{225 \text{ cal}} \right. = 4,830 \text{ Btu/hr}$$

$q_W = (8,400 - 1,000)$ cal/g mole

$$Q_W = \frac{7400}{} \left| \frac{25}{252} \right. = 735 \text{ Btu/hr}$$

(c) The point L_n is on a tie line with V_n. V_{n-1} is located by drawing an operating line through L_n and noting its intersection with the H-y phase envelope.

Starting at W in the stripping section, we move to V_W along a tie line, to L_m along an operating line, hence to V_m along a tie line, and finally to L_{m-1} along an operating line. At

$$V_{n-1}; y_{n-1} = 0.77$$

$$L_n; x_n = 0.54$$

$$V_m; y_m = 0.47$$

$$L_{m-1}; x_{m-1} = 0.23$$

7-7 ENRICHING TO STRIPPING SECTION TRANSITION

In Example 7–1, we demonstrated the method of stepping off plates in both the stripping and enriching sections of the column. Since the point P' is the appropriate difference point for the plates above the feed plate, and P'' for the plates below the feed plate, it follows that the transition from one difference point to the other occurs at the feed plate. Hence the problem of enriching to stripping plate transition is synonymous with the feed plate location problem.

In section 4–8 (page 83) we showed that in the McCabe-Thiele method the optimum transition point lies at the intersection of the enriching and stripping section operating lines, point P in (a) of Fig. 4–13. The analogous 'point' on the Ponchon diagram, Fig. 7–9, is the line $\overline{P'P''}$. Hence the optimum feed plate location is where the equilibrium tie line, plate 5, crosses $\overline{P'P''}$; hence plate 5 becomes the feed plate.

Points K and R in (b) and (c) of Fig. 4–13 represent, respectively,

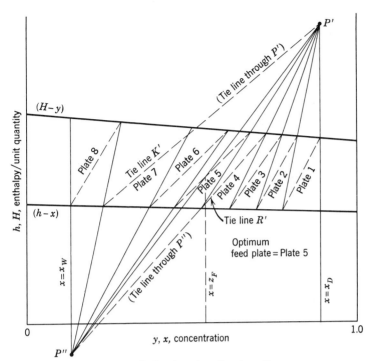

FIG. 7–9. Feed plate location, Ponchon diagram.

lower and upper limit feed plate locations; here the operating lines intersect the equilibrium curve. The exactly equivalent situation occurs in the Ponchon diagram at tie lines K' and R'. These tie lines coincide with operating lines; hence they represent pinch points just as points K and R did. Using the difference point P', it is impossible to move beyond tie line K', just as it is impossible to move past point K on the enriching section operating line in (b) of Fig. 4–13. In order to move further down the column, we must shift from the enriching to the stripping section operating line.

In Fig. 7–9 the saturated vapor and liquid lines are straight. It is easily proved that if the saturated vapor $(H-y)$ and saturated liquid $(h-x)$ lines are both straight *and* parallel, then the L/V ratios of Fig. 7–9 would be constant throughout the column; hence the Ponchon diagram gives answers equivalent to those of the McCabe-Thiele diagram at constant molal overflow.

Total reflux corresponds to a situation where we have no distillate or bottom products, and where the minimum number of plates are required to achieve a desired separation. It will be recalled that in the McCabe Thiele method this situation corresponded to having the operating line coincide with the $y = x$ line.

Figure 7–10 shows the total reflux condition on the Ponchon diagram. In the enthalpy-concentration diagram, the difference points P' and P'' lie at $+$ and $-$ infinity, respectively, since $y = x$ and $(h_D - q_D) = +\infty$, and $(h_W - q_W) = -\infty$.

Minimum reflux conditions correspond to a situation of minimum L/V, maximum product, infinite number of plates. When working with the McCabe-Thiele constructions we saw that minimum reflux was determined either by feed conditions or an equilibrium line pinch condition as in Fig. 4–16 on page 86.

Figure 7–11 demonstrates the analogous Ponchon constructions. In (*a*) where the minimum reflux ratio is determined by feed conditions, the difference points P' and P'' are located by extending the

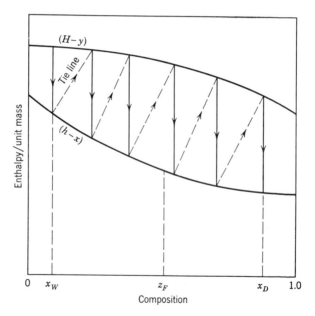

FIG. 7–10. Total reflux by Ponchon method.

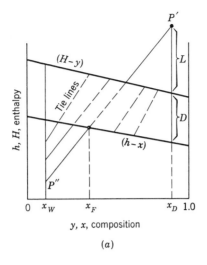

(a)

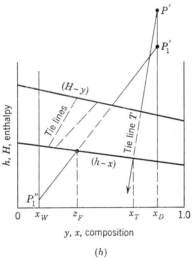

(b)

FIG. 7–11. Minimum reflux by Ponchon method. (a) Minimum reflux determined by the line through feed point, liquid feed. (b) Minimum reflux ratio determined by tie line between feed composition and overhead product.

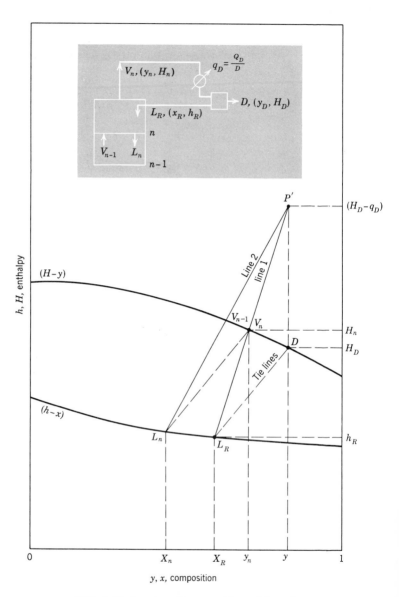

FIG. 7–12. Ponchon diagram with partial condenser.

equilibrium tie line through x_F to its intersections with the two difference points.

In (b) of Fig. 7–11, extension of the feed point tie line places the difference points at P_1' and P_1''. If we now attempt to step off plates, the pinch point manifests itself at tie line T. This tie line, which intersects the line $x = x_D$ at P', gives higher L/V ratios than the difference point P_1'. This suggests that the minimum reflux ratio in the enriching section is set by the highest intersection made by the steepest tie line in the section with the line $x = x_D$. Use of the difference point P' in stepping off plates gives an infinite number of plates with the pinch occurring at x_T. A differentially higher L/V ratio results in an operable design.

Point P'' is found by the intersection of $\overline{P'z_F}$ with $x = x_W$. If there is a tie line in the stripping section which gives a lower P'', this must be used; otherwise a pinch region will develop in the stripping section.

7–9 PARTIAL CONDENSERS

The construction of Fig. 7–12 corresponds to the enriching section with a partial condenser as shown in the insert. We see here that V_n and L_R are on the same operating line, and that L_R is in equilibrium with D.

EXAMPLE 7–2. A 59 mole percent vapor feed stream containing a 50 mole percent mixture of hexane-octane is to be separated into a distillate containing 95 mole% hexane and a bottoms containing 5 mole% hexane. The operation is to be carried out in a column with a reboiler and a partial condenser.

(a) What are the minimum number of plates the column must have to carry out the separation?

(b) At an L/D of $(1.5)(L/D)_{\text{minimum}}$ for the top plate, how many plates are required?

(c) Which is the optimum feed plate?

(d) Make a plot of number of theoretical stages versus the L/D ratio on the top plate and heat required per mole of bottoms.

Solution: (a) The minimum number of plates is established at total reflux. In this case the operating lines are vertical. Three theoretical stages are required (Fig. 7–13).

(b) There being no tie line which intersects the line $x = x_D$ above P_1', the equilibrium tie line through F serves to establish the difference

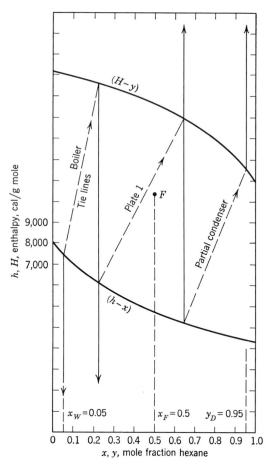

FIG. 7–13. Solution to Example 7–2 (part a).

points. (L/D) minimum at the top plate is $\overline{P_1'V_{n1}}/\overline{V_{n1}L_R} = 0.7$ (Fig. 7–14).

The point P' is located by drawing the line $\overline{L_RV_nP'}$ that such $\overline{P'V_{nl}}/\overline{V_nL_R} = (0.7)(1.5) = 1.05$.

Point P'' is located at the intersection of $\overline{P'F}$ with $x = x_W$.

The plates are stepped off in Fig. 7–15. Five stages are required; the feed is introduced on plate 2.

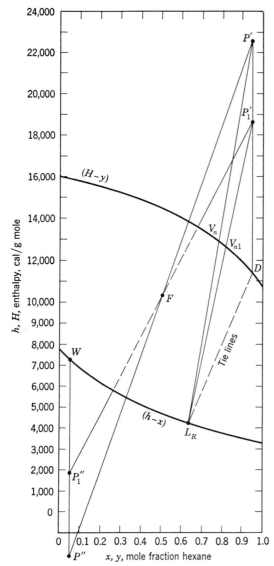

FIG. 7–14. Solution to Example 7–2 (part *b*).

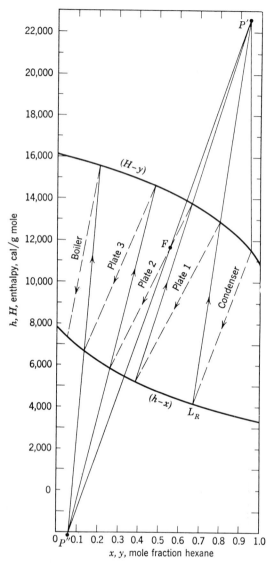

FIG. 7–15. Solution to Example 7–2 (part *b-c*).

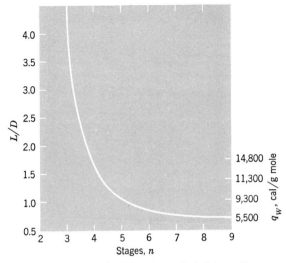

FIG. 7–16. Solution to Example 7–2 (part *d*).

(*c*) A plot of q_W and L/D versus the number of stages is given in Fig. 7–16. Note that L/D and q_W go to infinity as $n \to 3$, and that n goes to infinity as $L/D \to 0.7$ and $q_W \to 5,500$.

7–10 SIDE STREAMS AND MULTIPLE FEEDS

Although no new principles are involved, it is of considerable interest to examine the type of constructions required in multi-stream flow situations.

Consider a column of the type shown in Fig. 4–9 (page 78), but having the feed streams F_1 and F_2 and no side stream. Assuming that the distillate and bottoms compositions as well as the reflux ratio on the top plate are specified, we locate the point P' on Fig. 7–17. Next we turn our attention to the two feed streams. If F_1 and F_2 are mixed, the resultant stream $\mathscr{F} = F_1 + F_2$ can be located by material and energy balance methods, or by line segment ratios, since $\overline{F_1 \mathscr{F}} / \overline{F_2 \mathscr{F}} = F_2 / F_1$.

The difference point P'', which lies on the intersection of $x = x_W$ and the straight line through $\mathscr{F} P'$ is then located. We are now able to step off stages by using the upper difference point for the section of the column above F_1 and the lower one for the section below F_2.

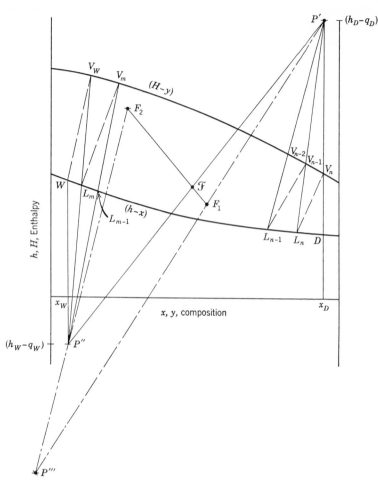

FIG. 7–17. Ponchon diagram with multiple feed and products.

In order to handle the section of the column between F_1 and F_2 we must find a new difference point.

The construction is shown in Fig. 7–17. For the section of the column between the top and a plate between F_1 and F_2, the net flow point must lie on a line through F_1 and P'. Similarly, the line through F_2 and P'' represents the net flow between a plate in the section between F_1 and F_2 and the bottom of the column. The intersection of the two balance lines occurs at P''', which is the difference point to be used in stepping off plates between F_1 and F_2. This may, of course, be verified by material and energy balances.

Another illustration may further clarify the procedures. Figure 7–18 shows a column having one side stream, S, along with the

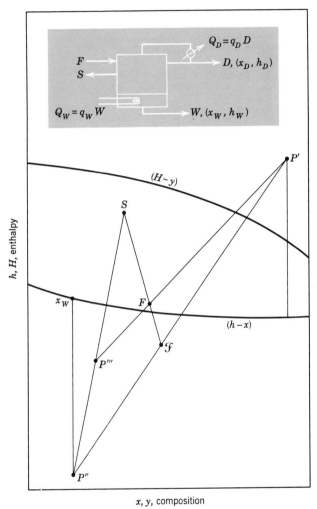

FIG. 7–18. Ponchon diagram with side stream.

usual feed, bottoms, and distillate. Again, it is assumed that the point P' has been located.

Since in this case $\mathscr{F} = F - S$, the point $\mathscr{F}$ in Fig. 7–18 is located so that $\overline{\mathscr{F}S}/\overline{\mathscr{F}F} = F/S$. Point P'' is located by extending the line $P'\mathscr{F}$ to its intersection with $x = x_W$.

The difference points P' and P'' are used in stepping off plates between the feed and top, and side stream and bottoms, respectively. Between F and S, the difference point P''' is used. The point P''' must be located at the intersection of $\overline{SP''}$ and $\overline{FP'}$.

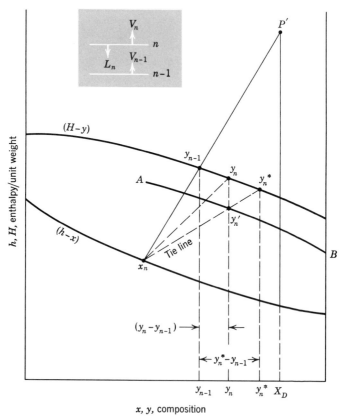

FIG. 7–19. Murphree plate efficiency on a Ponchon diagram.

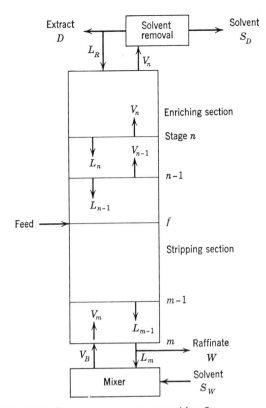

FIG. 7–20. Countercurrent extractor with reflux.

7–11 STAGE EFFICIENCIES AND ACTUAL NUMBER OF PLATES

The over-all and Murphree efficiencies were defined as

$$\text{Over-all efficiency} = \frac{\text{Theoretical contacts} \times 100}{\text{Actual contacts required}}$$

$$E_v = \text{Murphree (vapor phase) efficiency} = \frac{y_n - y_{n-1}}{y_n^* - y_{n-1}} \times 100 \tag{7-20}$$

Figure 7–19 is a graphical representation of Eq. 7–20 on a Ponchon diagram. If the stage efficiency is 100%, we would move from y_{n-1} to x_n, hence to y_n^*. If E_v is less than 100%, we would locate y_n by Eq. 7–20. In Fig. 7–20 it is assumed that y_n is a saturated vapor.

The same procedure used to establish the pseudo-equilibrium line on the McCabe-Thiele plot can be used in conjunction with the Ponchon method. If the Murphree efficiency is constant, a pseudo-equilibrium curve could be drawn through y_n' and other points located identically. This line, $\overline{AB}$, in conjunction with the difference points, could be used to step off stages.

7–12 THE PONCHON METHOD APPLIED TO EXTRACTION

We have seen how readily the McCabe-Thiele distillation plot can be applied to extraction, provided we adjust the coordinates to allow for the inert carriers. The same is true of the Ponchon diagrams.

In Fig. 7–20 we see a countercurrent extraction apparatus with reflux. The reflux is obtained by removing solvent from the extract and returning the solvent-saturated extract to the apparatus. Thus

TABLE 7–2
EQUIVALENT PARAMETERS IN DISTILLATION AND EXTRACTION

Distillation	Extraction
D = distillate	D = extract product (solvent-free basis)
Q = heat	S = mass solvent
Q_D = heat withdrawn in condenser	S_D = solvent withdrawn at top of column
$q_D = Q_D/D$	S_D/D
Q_W = heat added in reboiler	S_W = solvent added in mixer
$q_W = Q_W/W$	S_W/W
W = bottoms	W = raffinate (solvent-free basis)
L = saturated liquid	S = saturated raffinate
V = saturated vapor	V = saturated extract
A = more volatile component	A = solute to be recovered
B = less volatile component	B = component from which A is extracted
F = feed	F = feed
x = mole fraction A in liquid	X = mole or wt ratio of A (solvent-free), $A/(A + B)$
y = mole fraction A in vapor	$Y = S/(A + B)$

the extract phase undergoes added enrichment in the enriching section and it is possible to obtain extract concentrations much richer in solute than the extract in equilibrium with the feed.

To construct and use a Ponchon diagram for extraction problems it is convenient to consider the solvent in extractions analogous to the heat in distillations. Thus the solvent-free extract phase becomes analogous to the enthaply-rich vapor phase.[1] The similarity between the two processes is noted in Table 7–2. The most important difference between the two processes is in the choice of coordinates. In Fig. 7–21 the abscissa is on a solvent-free basis, $A/(A + B)$, as is the ordinate, $S/(A + B)$. Thus the coordinates of pure solvent are $X = 0$, $Y = $ infinity.

Other points of importance are shown in Fig. 7–21. If the solvent removed in the solvent removal converts the extract from the top stage V_n into the saturated streams D and L_R, then D and L_R can be located on the saturated extract line.

The two net flow points, P' and P'', are found as in distillation. P' is an imaginary mixture of solvent S_D and extract D. Hence it is located by adding S_D/D to the extract coordinate Y_D. Likewise, the net flow point P'' is obtained by taking the coordinates of W, (x_W, h_W) and subtracting the solvent, quantity S_W/W.

Since the feed is split as in distillation, the over-all balance line will be through the points P', P'', and the feed point F.

The ratio of line segments have their usual significance:
A (solvent-free) mass balance about the solvent remover,

$$V_n = D + L_R \qquad (7\text{--}21)$$

coupled with a solvent balance,

$$V_n Y_n - S_D = D Y_D + L_R Y_R \qquad (7\text{--}22)$$

yields

$$\frac{L_R}{D} = \frac{(Y_D + S_D/D) - Y_n}{Y_n - Y_R} = \frac{\overline{P'V_n}}{V_n L_R} \qquad (7\text{--}23)$$

Likewise, a solute balance about the solvent remover

$$V_n X_n = D X_D + L_R X_D$$

[1] B. P. Smith, *Design of Equilibrium Stage Processes*, McGraw-Hill Book Co., (1962), p. 193 shows that this analogy is useful only for ternary systems.

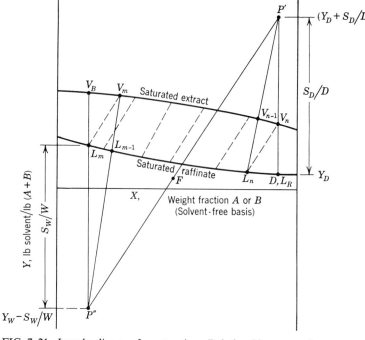

FIG. 7–21. Janecke diagram for extraction. Relationships among line segments

$$\frac{L_R}{D} = \frac{\overline{P'V_n}}{\overline{V_n L_R}} \; ; \qquad \frac{\overline{V}}{W} = \frac{\overline{L_m P''}}{\overline{V_B L_m}}$$

$$\frac{L_R}{V_n} = \frac{\overline{P'V_n}}{\overline{P'L'_R}} \; ; \qquad \frac{D}{W} = \frac{\overline{FP''}}{\overline{P'F}}$$

when solved simultaneously with Eq. 7–21 yields

$$\frac{L_R}{D} = \frac{X_D - X_n}{X_n - X_R} \tag{7-24}$$

Equation 7–24 combined with 7–23 gives

$$\frac{(Y_D + S_D/D) - Y_n}{X_D - Y_n} = \frac{Y_n - Y_R}{X_n - X_R}$$

which is the three-point form of the equation for a straight operating line between the two passing streams (Y_n, X_n) and (Y_R, X_R) and the difference point, P', $(Y_D + S_D/D, \; X_D)$. Equations analogous to those obtained for the stripping section in distillation (Eq. 7–15) and for the over-all balance line (Eq. 7–19) can also be made. Figure 7–21 includes a tabulation of the results of these balances.

Stepping off stages is accomplished exactly as in distillation. The intersection of a straight line through P' with the phase equilibrium lines marks the composition of two passing streams in the top of the column, viz., L_n and V_{n-1}. Likewise, a line through P'' cuts the envelope at points which denote the composition of passing streams in the stripping section. The significance of total and minimum reflux is also analogous.

eight / triangular diagrams in extraction

Triangular phase equilibrium diagrams, such as the one for the furfural (F)-ethylene glycol (G)-water (H) system (Fig. 2–6a, page 23), are commonly used in multistage cascade calculations. Either right triangle or equilateral triangles may be employed.

8–1 RIGHT TRIANGLE DIAGRAMS

In Fig. 8–1, the horizontal, vertical and diagonal axes represent weight fractions of G, F, and H, respectively.

There being only two independent composition variables, any point, such as A, can be located if two compositions are specified ($x_G = 0.43$, $x_F = 0.28$). The point A falls in the two phase region; hence, at equilibrium, the mixture separates into streams A' and A'', whose compositions are fixed by the intersection of the tie line with the phase envelope.

8–2 MATERIAL BALANCES ON A RIGHT TRIANGLE DIAGRAM

In stage n of Fig. 8–2, the streams V and L are termed the *overflow* and *underflow*. A component balance for glycol yields

$$L_{n-1}x_{n-1} + V_{n+1}y_{n+1} = V_n y_n + L_n x_n \qquad (8\text{–}1)$$

where the x and y refer to the same component. If the component be the solute (G), both x and y would be read on the horizontal axis of Fig. 8–1.

The mixing process in Fig. 8–2 is shown on Fig. 8–1. Here a

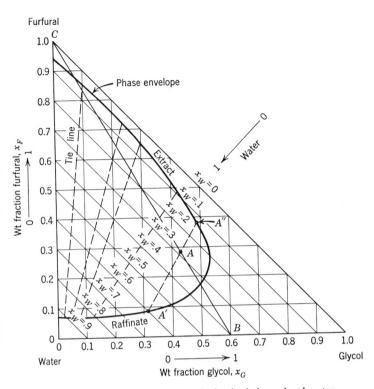

FIG. 8-1. Triangular diagram for furfural-ethylene glycol-water.

stream consisting of 60 wt % glycol in water, L_{n-1}, $x_{n-1} = 0.6$ (point B) is mixed with pure solvent (V_{n+1}, point C), in the ratio of 2.61 lb L_{n-1} to 1 lb solvent, $\overline{AB}/\overline{AC}$ = solvent/feed. The resulting mixture splits into the extract phase A'' and the raffinate phase in equilibrium with it, A' ($A'' = 48\%$ G, $A' = 32\%$ G).

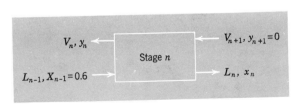

FIG. 8-2. An ideal stage.

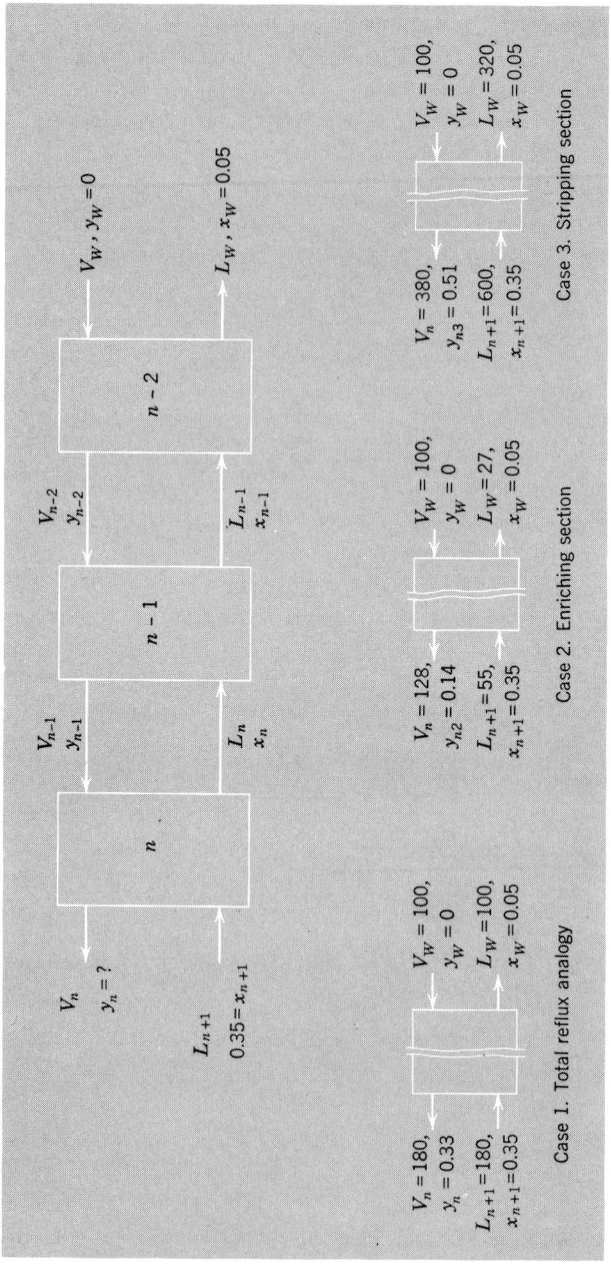

FIG. 8–3. Multi-stage countercurrent contactor.

V_W, $y_W = 0$

L_W, $x_W = 0.05$

V_{n-2}
y_{n-2}

L_{n-1}
x_{n-1}

$n-2$

V_{n-1}
y_{n-1}

L_n
x_n

$n-1$

V_n
$y_n = ?$

L_{n+1}
$0.35 = x_{n+1}$

n

$V_W = 100$,
$y_W = 0$

$L_W = 100$,
$x_W = 0.05$

$V_n = 180$,
$y_n = 0.33$

$L_{n+1} = 180$,
$x_{n+1} = 0.35$

Case 1. Total reflux analogy

$V_W = 100$,
$y_W = 0$

$L_W = 27$,
$x_W = 0.05$

$V_n = 128$,
$y_{n2} = 0.14$

$L_{n+1} = 55$,
$x_{n+1} = 0.35$

Case 2. Enriching section

$V_W = 100$,
$y_W = 0$

$L_W = 320$,
$x_W = 0.05$

$V_n = 380$,
$y_{n3} = 0.51$

$L_{n+1} = 600$,
$x_{n+1} = 0.35$

Case 3. Stripping section

8–3   OVER-ALL COLUMN BALANCES

Figure 8–3 represents a portion of a cascade for which the saturated terminal compositions $x_{n+1} = 0.35$, $x_W = 0.05$, and $y_W = 0$ (pure solvent) are specified. The ratio of solvent to feed is given as 0.56 in Case 1 ($V_W/L_{n-1} = 100/180$).

To make an over-all balance, we note that we may define the mixing point M by

$$M = V_W + L_{n+1} = V_n + L_W \qquad (8\text{--}2)$$

Since we know V_W and L_{n+1}, M can be located. The point on Fig. 8–4 corresponding to solvent/feed = 0.56 is M_1, and the point of intersection of a line through M_1 and L_W with the saturated extracts defines V_n at $y_n = 0.33$.

The compositions of all streams are now established and this, plus the ratio of solvent to feed, defines the material balance completely.

8–4   STRIPPING AND ENRICHING SECTION ANALOGIES

As in the Ponchon construction, we now invoke the concept of a difference point, P, which is the terminus of the operating line that marks the location of any two passing streams.

$$P = V_n - L_{n+1} = V_{n-1} - L_n = V_{n-2} - L_{n-1} = \ldots = V - L$$
$$(8\text{--}3)$$

We note, then, that according to this nomenclature the column of Fig. 8–3 functions as an enriching section if $V > L$, or as a stripping section if $L > V$. If $L = V$, the column may for convenience, be thought of as operating at total reflux (it will be shown later that some but not all total reflux conditions are fulfilled).

Case 1.   Total reflux analog $L = V$, solvent to feed ratio = 0.56. The mixing point is M_1 and the terminal composition $y_n = 0.33$. If we choose as a basis, a feed of 100 lb of solvent, the material balances are

$$V_W = 100, \ L_{n+1} = 100/0.56 = 180$$
$$V_W + L_{n+1} = 280 = L_W + V_n$$

F balance: $(0)(100) + (0.35)(180) = 0.05 L_W + 0.33 V_n$

Solving: $V_n = 180, \qquad L_W = 100$

As shown in Fig. 8–3, case 1 corresponds to $L = V$ throughout the column. If we now attempt to locate difference point, P_1, such

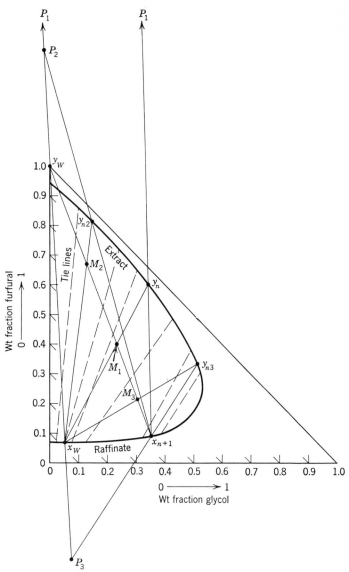

FIG. 8–4. Triangular diagram for furfural-ethylene glycol-water.

that $L = V$, or $\overline{P_1 V_n}/\overline{P' L_{n+1}} = 1$ and $\overline{P_1 V_n}/\overline{P' L_W} = 1$, we see (Fig. 8–4) that the points must be located at infinity, and that there is no intersection of the parallel operating lines.

Case 2. Enriching section; solvent to feed ratio > 0.56. If the solvent to feed ratio be 1.8, the mixing point is M_2, and the terminal composition $y_{n2} = 0.14$. The material balances, assuming again that $V_W = 100$, become:

$$V_W = 100, \quad L_{n+1} = 100/1.8 = 55$$

$$\text{F balance: } (0)(100) + (0.35)(55) = 0.05 L_W + 0.14 V_{n2}$$

$$\text{Solving: } V_{n2} = 128, \qquad L_W = 27$$

The net flow point, P_2 (Fig. 8–4) is located at the intersection of the material balance lines, $V_W/L_W = 100/27 = \overline{P_2 x_W}/\overline{P_2 y_W}$, and $V_{yn1}/L_{n+1} = 128/55 = \overline{P_2 x_{n+1}}/\overline{P_2 y_{n2}}$.

Case 3. Stripping section; solvent to feed ratio < 0.56. If the mixing point M_3 corresponds to a solvent per feed of 0.167, $y_{n3} = 0.51$, and if $V_W = 100$, $V_{n3} = 380$. $L_W = 320$, $L_{n+1} = 600$, the net flow point being P_3.

8–5 STEPPING OFF STAGES

Stepping off stages entails alternate use of equilibrium and material balance lines. In case 2 of section 8–4, the difference point is at P_2 and the terminal compositions are $x_{n+1} = 0.35$, $y_n = 0.14$, $x_W = 0.05$, and $y_W = 0$. If we start at the top of the column, we are on the operating line $\overline{P_2 x_{n+1}}$. We then move down to stage n along the equilibrium tie line through y_{n2}. Less than one stage is required to reach x_W, since the underflow composition from stage n is $< x_W = 0.05$ (the tie line is not shown for the sake of clarity).

8–6 TOTAL REFLUX, INFINITE STAGES

1. *Total reflux* in a distillation column is a condition where (a) the compositions of passing streams are equal, (b) a minimum number of stages are required, (c) $L = V$, (d) the difference point P is at infinity.

The "total reflux" situation, case 1 of section 8–4, mixing point M_1 on Fig. 8–4, is analogous to distillation, and meets conditions (c) and (d). This is because stream x_{n+1} is a feed stream rather than a reflux stream.

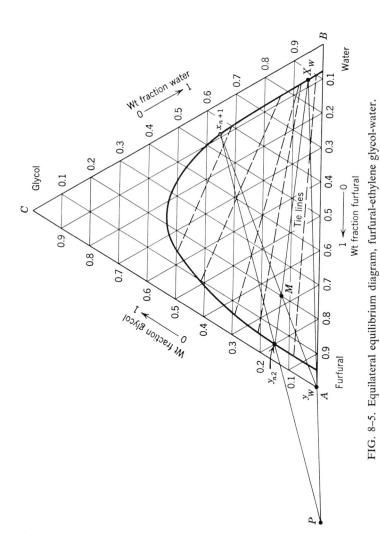

FIG. 8–5. Equilateral equilibrium diagram, furfural-ethylene glycol-water.

2. *Infinite Stages.* Case 3 of section 8–4 (difference point P_3) represents a pinch point on plate n, since the equilibrium tie line and operating lines coincide along $\overline{P_3 x_{n+1} y_{n3}}$.

If the net flow is up, no pinch point is encountered, an excess amount of solvent being used at all times.

3. *Minimum Reflux.* In extraction it is really more appropriate to talk about minimum solvent than minimum reflux. Study of Fig. 8–4 reveals that case 3, section 8–4 (M_3, P_3) represents the minimum solvent-infinite plate situation. If less solvent is used, point M_3 is lowered, P_3 is raised, and the column is inoperable.

It is interesting to note that in many ternary equilibrium diagrams the tie lines slope to the left rather than to the right. When this occurs, much of the situation is reversed, the pinch point falling in the region of P_2, not P_3; and, for the cases cited, the "enriching" and "stripping" sections of the column are reversed.

8–7 MULTI-STAGE EXTRACTIONS ON EQUILATERAL TRIANGLE DIAGRAMS

Countercurrent extraction calculations are readily made on triangular equilateral phase equilibrium diagrams, no new principles being involved. In Fig. 8–5 we see the solution to case 2, section 8–4.

The point y_{n2} is found by dividing the line between $y_W = 0$, $x_{n+1} = 0.35$ into the sections $\overline{M x_{n+1}}/\overline{M y_W} = 1.8$, and locating y_{n2} on the intersection of the line $\overline{M x_W}$ on the saturated extract phase envelope.

The difference point P is at the intersection of the balance lines through $\overline{x_{n+1} y_{n2}}$ and $\overline{x_W y_W}$.

It is seen that the separation can be carried out with one stage.

nine / multi-component mixtures and computer methods

In accordance with the phase rule, if we specify two thermodynamic variables in a two-phase, two-component system, the system parameters are fixed. In a three-component system an extra composition variable is introduced; hence we must specify $(n - 1)$ concentrations and either the temperature or pressure. It is now no longer possible to conveniently represent the data on a two-dimensional graph. For this reason, McCabe-Thiele and related graphical methods are not commonly used in problems involving more than two components.

The most general method for handling multi-component mixtures is by stage-to-stage calculations. The overhead product composition, feed stream, and reflux ratio are usually specified, so stepwise material balances, energy balances, and equilibrium relationship calculations can be made. The components of particular interest are termed "key" components. The two components whose concentrations are fixed at the top and bottom of the column are the *light* and *heavy keys* respectively (sometimes specifications call for a maximum concentration of light key in the bottoms or vice versa). Wherever the key-component concept can be used, certain simplified semi-empirical and/or graphical methods are applicable.

The labor involved in making stage-to-stage calculations in the case of multi-component mixtures is increased appreciably since a minimum of two pinch regions may exist in a column. Furthermore, the compositions of the product and bottoms stream are a function of the reflux ratio, thus making it even more difficult to calculate system parameters.

In the pre-1950 era, multi-component contactor design was accomplished by semi-empirical techniques, many of which are still widely used. In this chapter, we will examine some of these as well as computer methods.

9-1 USE OF K FACTORS IN MULTI-COMPONENT DISTILLATION

In the petroleum industry, multi-component distillation is a necessary and highly developed art. Fortunately, hydrocarbons are relatively well behaved, and liquid-vapor equilibrium data may, to a sufficiently high degree of precision, be presented in the form $y_i = K_i x_i$, the K (which has been discussed in section 2–3, page 19) being a function of temperature and pressure. Liquid-vapor equilibrium calculations for multi-component mixtures involving K factors generally degenerate into trial-and-error calculations. Given a liquid (or vapor) composition at constant P or T, we take trial vapor (or liquid) compositions, the right one being such that Σy_i (or Σx_i) equals one. The use of a K chart, Fig. 9–1, is demonstrated in Example 9–1.

EXAMPLE 9–1. A liquid mixture consisting of 10, 20, 30, and 40 mole percent of propane, butane, pentane, and hexane, respectively, is flash distilled at 100 psi and 200°F. What fraction of the stock leaves the stage as liquid, and what are the liquid and vapor compositions?

Solution: The K values for each component at 100 psi and 200°F are obtained from the Depriester charts and tabulated in column two of Table 9–1.

Basis: 1 mole of mixture.

The stoichiometry demands that

$$y_1 + y_2 + y_3 + y_4 = \sum_i y_i = 1$$

and

$$x_1 + x_2 + x_3 + x_4 = \sum_i x_i = 1$$

For each component, the x and y are related by

$$y_i/x_i = K_i \tag{9–1}$$

For 1 mole of total mixture, the moles of liquid L and vapor V are related by

$$L + V = 1$$

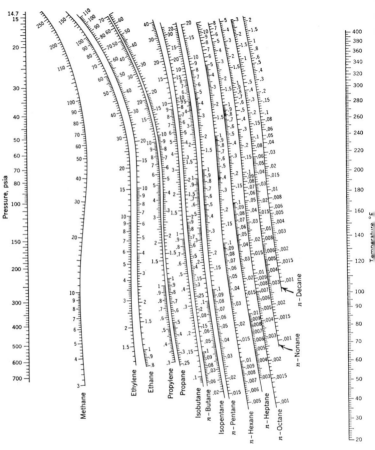

FIG. 9–1. Distribution coefficients ($K = y/x$) in light hydrocarbon systems, high-temperature range. [C. L. Depriester, *Chem. Eng. Progr. Symposium Ser.*, **49** (7), 1 (1953).]

The total moles of component i, n_i present in the mixture:

$$n_i = Lx_i + Vy_i = Lx_i + (1 - L)K_i x_i$$

Hence

$$x_i = \frac{n_i}{L + K_i(1 - L)} \qquad (9\text{–}2)$$

Equation 9–2 may be solved by trial and error. We assume values of L and calculate the x_i for each of the components and their

TABLE 9–1

SOLUTION TO EXAMPLE 9–1

Component	K	n(moles)	x $(L = 0.6)$	x $(L = 0.85)$	$y = Kx$
Propane	4.5	0.10	0.04	0.07	0.29
Butane	1.8	0.20	0.75	0.18	0.32
Pentane	0.75	0.30	0.37	0.31	0.23
Hexane	0.37	0.40	0.54	0.44	0.16
			$\Sigma x = 1.7$	$\Sigma x = 1.0$	$\Sigma y = 1.0$

sum, which must equal one. Two trials are shown in Table 9–1, an unsuccessful one at $L = 0.6$ (column 4) and the final one at $L = 0.85$ (column 5). The vapor compositions are then determined from $y_i = Kx_i$ (column 6).

9–2 MULTI-COMPONENT STAGEWISE CALCULATIONS

For a binary system, the problem of where to start a calculation was not acute. Relatively fool-proof graphical or analytical techniques could be used to achieve solutions. In a multi-component system, there are many ways of starting the calculation because the number of variables, which is proportional to the number of components, becomes very large.

In the case of distillation, the number of independent, controllable parameters are:[1]

1	Condensate condition
1	n stages above feed
1	m stages below feed
$(N - 1)$	number of components
1	Q_R reboiler load
1	Q_C condenser load
1	pressure
1	feed conditions
$N + 6$	total variables

For any given problem, if more than $N + 6$ variables are specified, an infinite number of solutions are attainable; for less than $N + 6$,

---

[1] Gilliland and Reed, *Ind. Eng. Chem.*, **32**, 1101 (1940).

no solution is possible, singular solutions existing only for $(N + 6)$ specifications.

Independent variables other than the ones specified may be used. Flows, reflux temperature, separation or recovery fraction,[1] or any other variable not defined by mass or energy balances or a fractionation equation may be used.

If we fix the feed composition, pressure, and heat losses, and specify that the total number of plates shall be a minimum, three variables remain to be assigned. One of these is usually the reflux ratio, the other two being residue and distillate concentrations. In a two-component system, specification of top and bottom concentrations is easily done; if the concentration of one component is specified, the relationship $\sum_1^2 y_i = \sum_1^2 x_i = 1$ is satisfied. In the more general case, where there are many ways of satisfying $\sum_1^n y_i = \sum_1^n x_i = 1$, only one of the calculated product and residue compositions can satisfy the material balances. In the event we specify a non-singular top concentration, we must expect our stagewise computation to produce an imbalance in the over-all material balance. In that case, we must specify another top composition and try again (if we are aiming for a particular bottoms). The computation is not quite as tortuous as it may appear because usually the key heavy components will be in low concentration in the distillate, and vice versa.

Example 9–2[2] demonstrates the application of these concepts.

EXAMPLE 9–2. A saturated liquid containing 60, 30, and 10 mole percent benzene, B, toulene, T, and xylene, X, is to be fractionated into a product containing not over 0.5 mole percent T, and a residue containing at the most 0.5 mole percent B. A $L/D = 2$ is to be used; constant molal overflow applies. The pressure is 1 atmosphere; Raoult's law is obeyed. Calculate the column parameters.

Solution: Basis: 100 moles of feed.

On the assumption that no X appears in the distillate, a material balance can be made. The results are given in Fig. 9–2, along with

---

[1] The fraction of a component appearing in a given stream.

[2] Adopted from Robinson and Gilliland, *Elements of Fractional Distillation*, p. 219, 4th ed., McGraw-Hill Book Co., 1950.

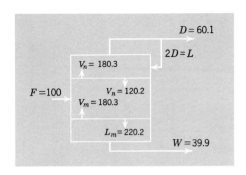

FIG. 9–2. Flow sheet for Example 9–2.

	F			D			W	
	Moles	%		Moles	%		Moles	%
B	60	60	B	59.8	99.5	B	0.2	0.5
T	30	30	T	0.3	0.5	T	29.7	74.4
X	10	10		60.1	100.0	X	10.0	25.1
	100	100					39.9	100.0

the vapor and liquid loads. Also required are the vapor pressure data of Fig. 9–3.

Operating lines for each component may be formuated. For benzene, in the stripping section:

$$y_{m,B} = \left(\frac{\overline{L}}{\overline{V}}\right) x_{(m-1),B} - \left(\frac{\overline{W}}{\overline{V}}\right) x_{W,B}$$

$$= \left(\frac{220.2}{180.3}\right) x_{(m-1),B} - \frac{39.9}{180.3}(0.005) \qquad (9\text{--}3)$$

toluene

$$y_{m,T} = 1.221 x_{(m-1),T} - 0.164 \qquad (9\text{--}4)$$

and xylene

$$y_{m,X} = 1.221 x_{(m-1),X} - 0.0555 \qquad (9\text{--}5)$$

The stagewise calculations are commenced in the stripping section by first determining the boiling point of the residue. This is accomplished in many cases by a trial-and-error procedure.

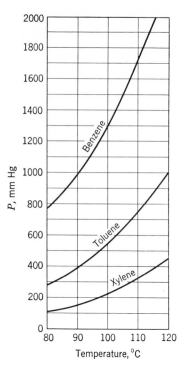

FIG. 9–3. Vapor pressure, benzene, toluene, xylene.

At the correct temperature, 116°C, the sum of the partial pressures is 760 mm.

Component	x_W	P(Fig. 9–3) (116°C)	$x_W P$	$y_W = x_W P/760$
B	0.005	2000	10	0.0131
T	0.744	873	650	0.855
X	0.251	400	100	0.132
			760	1.00

This procedure gives the composition of the vapor leaving the still. The liquid from the tray above the still is a passing stream with the vapor leaving the still; hence this liquid composition is obtained from the operating line equations (9–3, 9–4, and 9–5).

The vapor in equilibrium with the liquid leaving the first plate is now obtained, as for the residue, by use of a trial temperature and Raoult's law. The entire procedure is repeated until the ratio of B to T in the liquid phase straddles that ratio for the feed.

On the ninth plate above the still pot, the ratio of B/T is approximately that in the feed stream; this plate is the feed plate, and further stagewise calculations must employ the new enriching section operating lines:

$$y_{(n-1),B} = (L/V)x_{n,B} + (D/V)x_{D,B} = 0.667x_{n,B} + 0.332$$

$$y_{(n-1),T} = 0.667x_{n,T} + 0.0017$$

$$y_{(n-1),X} = 0.667x_{n,T}$$

Upon reaching the sixteenth plate, the benzene concentration exceeds 99.5%; thus, sixteen theoretical plates together with a reboiler and total condenser are necessary to effect the required separation.

9–3 ANALYSIS OF MULTI-COMPONENT SEPARATION CALCULATION METHODS[1]

In the *stage-to-stage calculation* method employed in Example 9–2, the conbitions for one stage of the process were fixed, and the rest of the variables were calculated by iteration procedures. In this case we started at an end stage; however, in other problems it may be necessary to converge on a known feed plate composition from both ends of the column.

A second approach is via a *group-method calculation*. In these methods the iterative stage-to-stage calculations are avoided by using product stream compositions along with certain approximations which permit the calculation of total stages directly. Usually, ideality and constancy of flows is assumed and limiting conditions are explored by using equations valid for a condition such as total or minimum reflux. The group methods represent short-cut design procedures and are fully explored in Chapter 10. In general, the

[1] Hanson, D. N., J. H. Duffin, and G. F. Sommerville, *Computation of Multistage Separation Processes*, Reinhold, 1962.

group methods give very poor results if the relative volatilities of the components are quite different; however, when this is the case, only a few stages are required. Group methods are most useful in situations calling for many stages, where the key components have close α's.

The third approach is by *successive approximations*. Generally, the number of stages for the process are fixed and, by one method or another, the achievable separations are calculated. The most general approach is to assume conditions of flow, temperature, or composition at each stage and then to calculate the unknown parameters. Since the originally assumed conditions are probably incorrect, repetitive corrective computations must be made until the flows, temperatures, and compositions are consistent. Many methods of corrective computation are available, the most desirable one for any given problem being the one which converges most rapidly. Successive approximation methods are ideally suited for digital computer analysis and represent by far the most useful and powerful of the multi-component calculation methods.

9–4 SUCCESSIVE APPROXIMATION METHODS—RELAXATION METHODS

The technique to be described determines the gradual change in the compositions on each plate from initial startup until steady state operation. The calculations are started by assuming stream compositions for each stage. The variation in the assumed composition for a short time interval is determined, the calculations being repeated until the compositions become independent of time. This type of calculation is termed a *relaxation* method.

Consider stage n of a column. During a short time interval of i minutes the change in moles of any component present in the liquid holdup of the plate is given by: Amount on Plate = Initial Amount + In Flow − Out Flow

$$Bx_{n,i+1} = Bx_{n,i} + V_{n-1}y_{n-1,i}$$
$$+ L_{n+1}x_{n+1,i} - V_n y_{n,i} - L_n x_{n,i} \quad (9\text{–}6)$$

where n = plate number
  $n + 1$ = plate above n
  $n - 1$ = plate below n
    i = particular time interval

$i + 1$ = next succeeding time interval of same duration as i
B = total moles of holdup on plate
V = vapor flow during the i minutes
L = liquid flow during the i minutes

Equation 9–6 states that the quantity of the component present on the stage during time interval from i to $(i + 1)$ is equal to that present during interval i, changed by the net amount of that component added and removed as a result of the liquid and vapor flows to and from the plate

Solving Eq. 9–6 to give composition $x_{n,i+1}$ in terms of the composition and flows for interval i,

$$x_{n,i+1} = x_{n,i} + 1/B[V_{n-1}y_{n-1,i} + L_{n+1}x_{n+1,i} - V_n y_{n,i} - L_n x_{n,i}]$$

$$(9\text{--}7)$$

Equations can be written for each component and each plate, including the still pot. The concept accepts the fact that V and L change from plate to plate; however, for the sake of simplifying the illustration, it will be assumed that L and V are constant, thus reducing Eq. 9–7 to

$$x_{n,(i+1)} = x_{n,i} + 1/B[Vy_{n-1,i} + Lx_{n+1,i} - Vy_{n,i} - Lx_{n,i}] \qquad (9\text{--}8)$$

The most convenient method of applying this approach is to assume that all the plate liquid compositions at time zero are equal to the feed composition. This choice is arbitrary and affects only the number of calculation time intervals necessary to achieve steady-state compositions. The first step is to calculate the composition of the liquid on the top plate at the end of the first time interval, using Eq. 9–8. In order to avoid difficulty, the choice of the time interval should be made such that V and L are approximately one-half to one-tenth of the plate holdup. Equation 9–8 is then used to calculate the liquid composition on the plate below the top and so on down to the reboiler. The calculations may be started at the reboiler and taken up the column, or they may be started at any plate and worked out to the top plate and the reboiler.

When all the liquid plate calculations have been computed for the first time interval, a second time interval is computed. The computations are repeated for successive time intervals until steady-state compositions are reached. In general, most of the plate compositions change rapidly at first and then gradually approach steady state values. To find the optimum arrangement of number of plates, reflux ratio, feed conditions, etc., it is only necessary to specify various values for these parameters and to solve the problem again.

The information required to carry out such a calculation for a specific distillation problem is: (1) number of theoretical plates, (2) reflux ratio, (3) feed, overhead, and bottoms flow rates, (4) location of feed, (5) initial plate compositions, (6) holdup on each plate, and (7) equilibrium and thermodynamic data. It should be noted that the final solution for plate compositions is independent of the initial plate compositions chosen, or the amount of liquid holdup assigned to each plate. These choices affect only the number of time intervals before the steady-state values are obtained.

Application of this method is demonstrated by again considering the problem of Example 9–2.

The problem involved a theoretical sixteen-plate distillation column equipped with a reboiler which behaves as an additional theoretical stage. The feed is a saturated liquid, 60 mole percent benzene, 30 mole percent toluene, and 10 mole percent xylene. We shall assume that the feed plate is the ninth plate from the bottom.

Reflux ratio $2:1 = L:D$

60.1% of the feed is to be taken overhead as product.

A time interval is arbitrarily chosen such that the moles of feed entering the column during this time interval is 10; therefore,

Overhead quantity during this time interval = 6.01 moles

Bottoms quantity during this time interval = 3.99 moles

Assuming constant molal overflow (it is emphasized that this assumption is for the sake of clarity of presentation and is not required), the vapor and liquid flow rates at a reflux ratio of $2:1$ are found:

$$V_n = 18.03 \text{ moles during time interval}$$
$$L_n = 12.02 \text{ moles during time interval}$$

Below the feed plate,

$$\bar{V}_m = 18.03 \text{ moles during time interval}$$
$$\bar{L}_m = 22.02 \text{ moles during time interval.}$$

The liquid holdup, B, on each plate is arbitrarily taken to be 50 moles. This meets the requirement that the V and L flow during the time interval are one-half to one-tenth of the liquid holdup on the plates.

The plate liquid compositions are all assumed to be initially equal to the feed composition: 60 mole percent benzene, 30 mole percent toluene, 10 mole percent xylene. If x_R be the reflux from a total condenser, the top plate (plate n) compositions for $i = 0$ are given in the accompanying table.

PLATE n AT $i = 0$

Component	$x_{n,0}$	$y_{n,0}$	$x_{R,0}$	$y_{n-1,0}$
Benzene	0.600	0.816	0.816	0.816
Toluene	0.300	0.160	0.160	0.160
Xylene	0.100	0.024	0.024	0.024

The vapor compositions $y_{n,0}$ and $y_{n-1,0}$ are determined by a boiling point calculation, using the vapor-liquid equilibrium data for the system. Thus the compositions in the following tables are obtained.

PLATE $n - 1$ AT $i = 0$

Component	$x_{n-1,0}$	$y_{n-1,0}$	$x_{n,0}$	$y_{n-2,0}$
Benzene	0.600	0.816	0.600	0.816
Toluene	0.300	0.160	0.300	0.160
Xylene	0.100	0.024	0.100	0.024

PLATE $n - 2$ AT $i = 0$

Component	$x_{n-2,0}$	$y_{n-2,0}$	$x_{n-1,0}$	$y_{n-3,0}$
Benzene	0.600	0.816	0.600	0.816
Toluene	0.300	0.160	0.300	0.160
Xylene	0.100	0.024	0.100	0.024

This is the same for each plate down to and including the reboiler. The liquid compositions at $i = 1$ interval are now calculated. Consider plate n, at $i = 1$, applying Eq. 9–8,

BENZENE:

$$x_{n,1} = x_{n,0} + 1/B[Vy_{n-1,0} + Lx_{R,0} - Vy_{n,0} - Lx_{n,0}]$$
$$= 0.600 + 1/50[(18.03)(0.816) + 12.02(0.816)$$
$$-18.03(0.816) - 12.02(0.600)]$$

$$x_{n,1} = 0.652$$

TOLUENE:

$$x_{n,1} = 0.300 + 1/50[18.03(0.160) + 12.02(0.160)$$
$$-18.03(0.160) - 12.02(0.300)]$$

$$x_{n,1} = 0.266$$

XYLENE:

$$x_{n,1} = 0.082$$

Applying Eq. 9–8 at the top plate again, for $i = 2$ intervals, gives:

BENZENE:

$$x_{n,2} = 0.652 + 1/50[18.03(0.816) + 12.02(0.848)$$
$$-18.03(0.848) - 12.02(0.652)]$$

$$x_{n,2} = 0.688$$

TOLUENE:

$$x_{n,2} = 0.266 + 1/50[18.03(0.160) + 12.02(0.132)$$
$$-18.03(0.132) - 12.02(0.266)]$$

$$x_{n,2} = 0.244$$

XYLENE:

$$x_{n,2} = 0.068$$

Therefore, the top plate compositions at $i = 1$ intervals are given in the accompanying table.

PLATE n AT $i = 1$

Component	$x_{n,1}$	$y_{n,1}$	$x_{R,1}$	$y_{n-1,1}$
Benzene	0.652	0.848	0.848	0.816
Toluene	0.266	0.132	0.132	0.160
Xylene	0.082	0.020	0.020	0.024

Applying Eq. 9–8 to plate $n - 1$ gives for $i = 1$,

BENZENE:

$$x_{n-1,1} = x_{n-1,0} + 1/B[Vy_{n-2,0} + Lx_{n,0} - Vy_{n-1,0} - Lx_{n-1,0}]$$
$$= 0.0600 + 1/50[18.03(0.816) + 12.02(0.600)$$
$$- 18.02(0.816) - 12.02(0.600)]$$
$$= 0.600$$

TOLUENE:

$$x_{n-1,1} = 0.300$$

XYLENE:

$$x_{n-1,1} = 0.100$$

The liquid composition on $n - 1$ is unchanged because in the first time interval only plate n is affected.

PLATE $n - 1$ AT $i = 1$

Component	$x_{n-1,1}$	$y_{n-1,1}$	$x_{n,1}$	$y_{n-2,1}$
Benzene	0.600	0.816	0.652	0.816
Toluene	0.300	0.160	0.266	0.160
Xylene	0.100	0.024	0.082	0.024

The compositions on all plates below $n - 1$ at $i = 1$ are the same as at $i = 0$.

PLATE n AT $i = 2$

Component	$x_{n,2}$	$y_{n,2}$	$x_{R,2}$	$y_{n-1,2}$
Benzene	0.688	0.866	0.866	0.814
Toluene	0.244	0.116	0.116	0.175
Xylene	0.068	0.018	0.018	0.011

Plate $n - 1$ at $i = 2$ intervals:

BENZENE:

$$x_{n-1,2} = 0.600 + 1/50[18.03(0.816) + 12.02(0.652)$$
$$- 18.03(0.816) - 12.02(0.600)]$$
$$= 0.613$$

Multi-component Mixtures and Computer Methods | *159*

TOLUENE:

$$x_{n-1,2} = 0.325$$

XYLENE:

$$x_{n-1,2} = 0.062$$

The compositions on plate $n - 1$ at the end of 2 time intervals are given in the next table.

PLATE $n - 1$ AT $i = 2$

Component	$x_{n-1,2}$	$y_{n-1,2}$	$x_{n,2}$	$y_{n-2,2}$
Benzene	0.613	0.834	0.688	0.816
Toluene	0.292	0.155	0.244	0.160
Xylene	0.095	0.011	0.068	0.024

The compositions on the plates below $n - 1$ are unchanged at $i = 2$.

The computation is now continued for $i = 3$ and then repeated for successive time intervals until the compositions on all plates

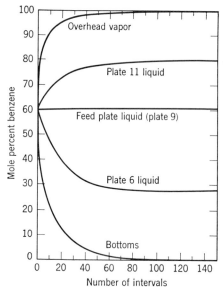

FIG. 9–4. Concentration of benzene as a function of time intervals.

remain constant. These steady-state values of composition represent the solution to the design problem.

The results of this illustrated problem, obtained on a digital computer, are shown in Fig. 9–4 for the overhead product, bottoms product, feed plate, a typical enriching section plate, and a stripping section plate.

If this distillation problem involved the design of a new facility, it would be necessary to resolve the problem with different numbers of plates, feed location, reflux ratios, feed conditions, etc. The optimum design from a cost point of view can then be shown.

9–5 SUCCESSIVE APPROXIMATION METHODS—MASS BALANCE METHODS[1]

If the stages, stage temperatures, total amounts of tops and bottoms, stage flows, and feed parameters are held as independent variables, and the total *amount* of a component in the bottom product is assumed, a stage-to-stage calculation will give the corresponding amount of this component in the top stage. An over-all mass balance can then be made, any imbalance being attributed to the assumed bottoms flow. Hence,

$$(Bx_B)_{\text{assumed}} = (Bx_B)_{\text{true}} + \mathscr{E}_B$$

where $\mathscr{E}_B$ is the error made in the bottom product. The corresponding error in the calculated product flow, $\mathscr{E}_D$, is

$$\mathscr{E}_B + \mathscr{E}_D + (Bx_B)_{\text{true}} + (Dx_D)_{\text{true}} = (Bx_B)_{\text{assumed}} + (Dx_D)_{\text{assumed}}$$

If $\mathscr{E}_B$ is defined, so is $\mathscr{E}_D$, and so is every other error, and therefore a new composition map for the component in question can be found. This process is repeated for each component. Next, it is necessary to check the assumed temperatures by calculating the bubble points of the mixtures on each tray. Now, using the corrected temperature map, the entire calculation is repeated.

For a column with a total reflux condenser returning feed at saturation, where there are N + 6 variables,

1. The variables set are:
   Feed enthalpy and composition
   Pressure

[1] Hanson et al., *op. cit.*

Stages above feed
Stages below feed
Reflux
Amount of product

2. Liquid flows and temperatures on each stage are assumed.

3. Sets of composition corresponding to the flow and temperature profiles are calculated.

4. Compositions of products are corrected to correspond to the set product amounts.

5. The composition of the stages above and below the feed are corrected.

6. The temperature map is corrected.

7. The calculations are repeated to convergence.

This scheme can readily be applied to gas absorption columns. For a plate column operating without reflux and with feed streams entering at the ends of the column, there are only $N + 3$ degrees of freedom. Hence,

1. The variables set are:
   Feed enthalpy and condition
   Pressure
   Stages

2. Liquid flows and temperatures on each stage are chosen.
Steps 4 to 7 in the calculation are the same as in distillation.

This particular iterative scheme is especially applicable to situations where the separation factors are not a function of composition. For particular non-ideal systems the mass balance method does not converge very well, and relaxation methods are said to be preferred.

When applied to liquid-liquid extraction, the iterative solutions are simplified, since a constant temperature can nearly always be assumed. Then we need only:

1. Assume flows.

2. Calculate compositions.

3. Correct the flows and repeat to convergence.

In the mass balance method, the energy balances served to correct the flow map. Alternatively, we might have started with a constant net heat flow and developed an accurate heat flow map, using mass balances to generate corrections. These so-called energy balance methods are described by Hanson et. al., *op. cit.*

9–6 OTHER PUBLISHED METHODS[1]

(a) *Lewis and Matheson.* Product and bottoms composition as well as reflux ratio are assumed; the calculations are then made from top and bottom, converging on the feed stream.

(b) *Thiele and Geddes.* Starting with an assumed number of equilibrium plates, reflux ratio, and tray temperatures, the terminal stream compositions (unknown) are carried as a function of internal stream compositions. The final mesh at the feed plate gives the bottom product composition and the distillate product is determined by material balance.

[1] R. N. Maddox, *Chem. Eng.*, **139** (Dec. 11, 1961).

ten / mechanical design

In a column design we must specify parameters such as column diameter, stage spacing, stage layout, and stage efficiency. These parameters in turn influence, or are influenced by, factors such as the physical properties of the streams, allowable vapor and liquid velocities, etc. Overriding all of this is the fact that the sum of the operating and construction costs must be kept at a minimum.

In this chapter we outline some of the industrial design methods for sizing and designing stagewise contactors. These methods, like all design methods in engineering, are based partly on theory and partly on empirical performance data. To the novice, it may fallaciously appear that some of the methods are strictly of the cook-book variety. Further study of the literature cited will convincingly demonstrate that the design methods recommended are solidly rooted in theory and that their intelligent application demands a full understanding of fundamentals.

10-1 SHORT-CUT METHODS—ECONOMICS[1]

A convenient method for minimizing total costs of a distillation column is based on a technique first developed by Colburn[2] and later revised by Happel.[3] Column costs include:

1. Cost of the column, per pound mole of distillate:

$$C_c = (C_1 SN)/(ED)$$
$$S = V/G_a = D(1 + R)/G_a \qquad (10\text{--}1)$$
$$C_c = C_1 N(1 + R)/EG_a$$

[1] From original notes by F. J. Connelly, Hercules Powder Co. (1960).
[2] Colburn, A. P., Lecture notes, University of Delaware (1943).
[3] Happel, J., *Chem. Eng.*, **144** (July 14 1958).

A 104-tray absorber and demethanizer at the Cologne Refinery of Standard Oil Co. (N.J.). The unit contains 4-in. circular bubble caps and processes 50,000 MT/year. Photo courtesy of Standard Oil Co. (N.J.).

where C_c = cost of column per lb mole of distillate
C_1 = amortized incremental column investment cost, dollars/ sq ft-plate-year
S = sq ft, tower cross-section
N = theoretical stages
E = plate efficiency
D = distillate rate, lb mole/hr
V = vapor rate, lb mole/hr
G_a = allowable vapor velocity, lb mole/hr sq ft
R = reflux ratio, liquid returned to column per lb mole of product

2. Condenser and reboiler cost:

$$C_{CR} = (C_2 H)/hD$$

$$H = V/G_b = D(1 + R)/G_b \qquad (10\text{--}2)$$

$$C_{CR} = C_2(1 + R)/hG_b$$

where C_{CR} = condenser and reboiler cost per mole of distillate
C_2 = amortized incremental tubular investment cost, dollars/sq ft-year
H = tubular equipment area, sq ft
h = operating hours per year
G_b = vapor handling capacity of tubular equipment, lb mole/sq ft-hour

3. Steam and cooling cost per mole of distillate (feed at boiling point):

$$C_{CS} = (C_3 V)/D = C_3(1 + R)$$

where C_{CS} = cost of steam and cooling per mole of distillate
C_3 = cost of steam and coolant, dollars/lb mole of distillate

4. Total cost:

$$C_t = \frac{C_1 N(1 + R)}{EG_a} + \frac{C_2(1 + R)}{hG_b} + C_3(1 + R) \qquad (10\text{--}3)$$

The rate of change of total cost with reflux ratio is

$$\frac{dC_T}{dR} = \frac{C_1 N}{EG_a} + \frac{C_1(1 + R)}{EG_a}\frac{dN}{dR} + \frac{C_2}{hG_b} + C_3 \qquad (10\text{--}4)$$

From purely economic considerations the optimum reflux ratio, R_0, and the optimum number of plates, N_0, correspond to the minimum

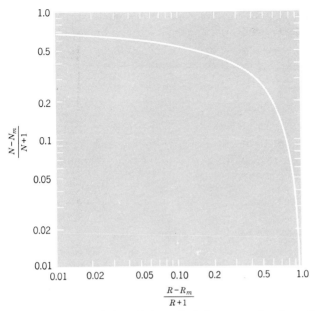

FIG. 10-1. Gilliland correlation of theoretical plates as a function of reflux ratio. [E. R. Gilliland, *Ind. Eng. Chem.*, **32**, 1220 (1940).]

in Eq. 10-4.

$$1 + R_0 = \frac{N_0 + [C_2/hG_b + C_3][EG_a/C_1]}{-dN/dR} = \frac{N_0 + F}{-dN/dR} \quad (10\text{-}5)$$

the F being defined by the equation.

To solve Eq. 10-5 we need a plot of N versus R. The most convenient plot, the one due to Gilliland, Fig. 10-1, correlates the number of plates with reflux ratio at any given minimum number of plates, N_m, and R_m, the minimum reflux ratio.[1]

Taking slopes of Fig. 10-1, Happel constructed Fig. 10-2. It is apparent from this figure that the optimum number of trays is almost universally from 2 to 3 times the minimum number. The value 2.5 is useful for rapid approximations. The corresponding optimum reflux ratio (not shown) is only a few percent greater than the minimum. If the accuracy of the equilibrium data is questionable, a somewhat higher than optimum reflux ratio (up to 1.5 R_m) can be employed at little additional cost.

[1] E. R. Gilliland, *Ind. Eng. Chem.*, **32**, 1220 (1940).

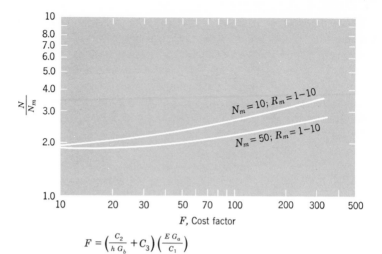

$$F = \left(\frac{C_2}{h\,G_b} + C_3\right)\left(\frac{E\,G_a}{C_1}\right)$$

FIG. 10–2. Optimum number of theoretical trays. [Happel, *J. Chem. Eng.*, **144** (July 14, 1958).]

10–2 SHORT-CUT METHODS—ESTIMATION OF THEORETICAL PLATES AND REFLUX RATIO

The rapid and convenient Gilliland method for determining the relationship between N and R requires a knowledge of the minimum stages N_m and reflux ratio R_m.

1. *Minimum number of plates.* The Fenske equation (4–33) applies to multi-component as well as binary systems. In terms of the light and heavy keys and their relative volatilities:

$$N_m = \frac{\log\left(\frac{x_1}{x_2}\right)_D\left(\frac{x_2}{x_1}\right)_W}{\log \alpha_{\text{avg}}} \qquad (10\text{–}6)$$

where x_1 = mole fraction of more volatile or light key

$\quad\ x_2$ = mole fraction of less volatile or heavy key

$\quad \alpha_{\text{avg}} = \sqrt{\alpha_D \alpha_W}$ average relative volatility between top and bottom of column or the mean ratio of light key to heavy key in multi-component mixtures.

$$\alpha = \frac{y_1/x_1}{y_2/x_2}$$

2. *Minimum reflux ratio*, $L/D = R_m$. Of the various methods for locating the pinch points and the corresponding R_m in multicomponent systems, the one due to Underwood is perhaps the most commonly used.[1] It is valid for ideal systems having constant relative volatilities. In using the method, we proceed as follows:

(a) Solve Eq. 10–7 for the value of θ which lies between the relative volatilities of the key components (other values of θ are discarded).

$$\frac{\alpha_1 z_{F_1}}{\alpha_1 - \theta} + \frac{\alpha_2 z_{F_2}}{\alpha_2 - \theta} + \cdots \frac{\alpha_n z_{F_n}}{\alpha_n - \theta} = 1 - q \qquad (10-7)$$

where z_F = mole fraction of component n in feed.

q = thermal condition of feed, i.e., heat to vaporize 1 mole of feed/molar latent heat of feed.

Having obtained θ, we calculate the minimum L/D, R_m, from Eq. 10–8.

$$R_m + 1 = \frac{\alpha_1 x_{D_1}}{\alpha_1 - \theta} + \frac{\alpha_2 x_{D_2}}{\alpha_2 - \theta} + \cdots \frac{\alpha_n x_{D_n}}{\alpha_3 - \theta} \qquad (10-8)$$

10–3 SHORT-CUT METHODS—FEED PLATE LOCATION

Although more sophisticated methods are available, direct use of the Fenske equation gives a rather reliable answer.[2]

1. Find the number of plates required between feed and distillate at total reflux (by Eq. 10–6).

2. Find the total number of plates required (by Eq. 10–6).

3. Assume that the ratio of rectification to total plates applies at finite as well as total reflux ratios.

10–4 SHORT-CUT METHODS—MECHANICAL DESIGN

Most of the general factors entering into the mechanical design of columns were discussed in Chapter 3. Typical trays were shown in Figs. 3–7 and 3–8 (pages 42 and 43). A general correlation for determining plate spacing as a function of allowable vapor velocity is given in Fig. 10–3.[3] The correlation is given in terms of weir length, liquid flow, liquid depth on the plate, and the crest over the weir.

[1] A. J. V. Underwood, *Chem. Eng. Prog.*, **44**, 603 (1948).
[2] S. R. M. Ellis, *Pet. Ref.*, **33**, 307 (1954).
[3] Courtesy of F. J. Connelly, Hercules Powder Company (1960).

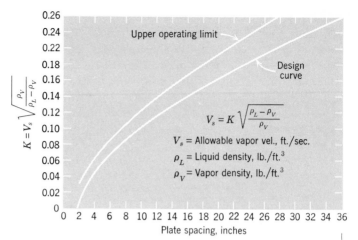

FIG. 10–3. Allowable vapor velocity and tray spacing in bubble cap and perforated plate columns.

Table 1

t	δ
24	4
18	3
12	2
<12	0

Allowance for liquid depth at plate spacing $\leqq 24''$

(1) $T = t - d_0 + \delta$

t = Installed tray spacing—inches
T = Tray spacing corrected for liquid depth—inches
$d_0 = h_1 + h_w$ = total depth of clear liquid, in.
δ = Constant from Table 1
A when $d_0 > \delta$, enter chart with T from Eq. 1 above.
B when $d_0 \leqq \delta$, enter chart with t

$h_1 = (Q/2.98Z_w)^{2/3}$
Q = GPM liquid downflow
Z_w = Length of weir, in.
h_w = Overflow weir height, in.
h_1 = Crest over weir, in.

10–5 SHORT-CUT METHODS—COLUMN EFFICIENCY

Figure 10–4, which is replotted from the data given by O'Connell, is an empirical correlation of over-all column efficiency as a function of relative volatility and liquid viscosity. If sufficient data is available, the A.I.Ch.E. Plate Efficiency Study may be used.[1] This treatise takes into account such variables as contact time on the tray, eddy diffusivity, liquid travel, liquid head, entrainment, weir height, etc.

[1] *Bubble-Tray Design Manual*, American Institute of Chemical Engineers, New York.

EXAMPLE 10–1. A perforated plate column for handling 550 lb moles/hr of the following mixture is to be designed:

Component	MW	Mole %	α
A	32	30	1.75
B	46	20	1.0
C	60	15	0.5
D	74	35	0.2

Vapor Pressure of B

Temp	60	70	80	90	100
P_B^0 mm Hg	340	540	810	1180	1680

Liquid density at b.p. — 45 lb/cu ft
Liquid viscosity at b.p. = 0.3 centipoises

The feed, which is 25 mole% vapor, is separated continuously at atmospheric pressure into an overhead product containing 95 mole percent A and 5 mole percent B and a residue containing 5 mole percent A (other components as calculated). Assume constant α and ideal solutions. Calculate: (a) distillate and residue rates, (b)

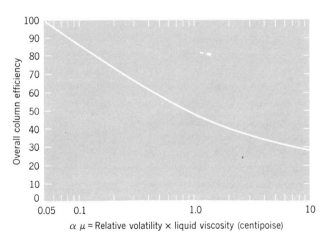

FIG. 10–4. Over-all column efficiency of fractionation column. [Data from O'Connell, *Trans. A. I. Ch. E.*, 42, 741 (1946).]

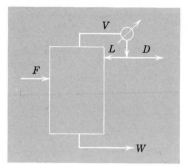

FIG. 10–5. Flow sheet for Example 10–1.

	F			D			W	
	Moles	%		Moles	%		Moles	%
A	165	30	A	144	95	A	21	5
B	110	20	B	8	5	B	102	25.8
C	83	15		—	—	C	83	20.7
D	192	35		152	100	D	192	48.5
	550	100					398	100.0

number of actual plates, (c) reflux ratio, (d) top and bottom temperature, (e) column diameter, (f) plate spacing and column height, (g) feed plate location.

Solution: (a) The results of the material balance calculations are given in the flow sheet, Fig. 10–5, on the basis of one hour.

(b) The minimum number of plates is calculated by using the Fenske equation (10–6).

$$\alpha_{avg} = \frac{\alpha \text{ light key}}{\alpha \text{ heavy key}} = \frac{1.75}{1.0} = 1.75$$

$$N_m = \frac{\log\left[\left(\frac{x_1}{x_2}\right)_D \left(\frac{x_2}{x_1}\right)_W\right]}{\log \alpha_{avg}} = \frac{\log\left[\left(\frac{0.95}{0.05}\right)\left(\frac{0.258}{0.05}\right)\right]}{\log 1.75} = 8.2$$

Using a $N/N_m = 2.5$, and assuming the reboiler accounts for one stage, the actual number of plates $= (2.5)(7.2) = 18$. From Fig. 10–4, the column efficiency at $\alpha\mu = (1.75)(0.3) = 0.525$ is 0.58. Therefore, the actual number of plates is $18/0.58 = 31$.

(c) The minimum reflux ratio is obtained by Underwood's method, Eq. 10–7; substituting,

$$\alpha_1 = 1.75 \qquad \alpha_2 = 1 \qquad \alpha_3 = 0.5 \qquad \alpha_4 = 0.2 \qquad q = 0.75$$

$$z_{F1} = 0.3 \qquad z_{F2} = 0.2 \qquad z_{F3} = 0.15 \qquad z_{F4} = 0.35$$

we obtain $\theta = 1.25$.

Substituting in Eq. 10–8, $R_m = (L/D)_{min} = 2.13$.

The actual L/D is obtained from Fig. 10–1. At

$$\frac{N - N_m}{N + 1} = \frac{19 - 8.2}{20} = 0.54$$

$$\frac{(L/D) - (L/D)_{min}}{(L/D) + 1} = 0.9, \text{ and } L/D = 2.45.$$

(d) The top tower temperature is set by the dew point.

$$P_B{}^0 = \frac{P}{\Sigma \, \alpha_x} = \frac{760}{(1.75)(0.95) + (1.0)(0.05)} = 444 \text{ mm}$$

This corresponds to a temperature of 66°C. The bottom temperature is set by the bubble point,

$$P_B{}^0 = \frac{P}{\Sigma \, \alpha_x}$$

$$= \frac{760}{(1.75)(0.05) + (1.0)(0.258) + (0.5)(0.208) + (0.2)(0.485)}$$

$$= 1390 \text{ mm}$$

This corresponds to a temperature of 94°C.

(e) Let us assume a plate spacing of 18 in. From Fig 10–3,

$$K = 0.17 = V_s \sqrt{\frac{\rho_V}{\rho_L - \rho_V}} \, .$$

Using average MW and temperatures to obtain ρ_V, $V_s = 3.91$ ft/sec. The total vapor load is $V = L + D = D + (L/D)D = 152 + 2.45(152) = 526$ moles/hr.

Since $Q = V_s \rho_V A$, solving for A, $A = 14.1$ sq ft.

Tower diameter = ~ 4.2 ft.

(f) The plate spacing was assumed to be 18 in. We might have chosen other plate spacings and still have designed an operable column. An experience factor as well as a close economic analysis is required to effect the best choice. Correlations such as the one

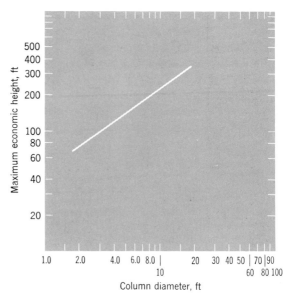

FIG. 10–6. Economic column heights. [After Stogens, *Brit. Chem. Eng.*, **6**, 182 (March 1961).]

shown in Fig. 10–6 are useful in this respect. The minimum column height is $(31)(1.5) = 46$ ft.

(*g*) for the rectifying section of the column:

$$N_m = \frac{\log \left(\dfrac{0.95}{0.05}\right)\left(\dfrac{0.20}{0.30}\right)}{\log 1.75} = 4.55$$

The ratio of rectifying plate/total plates $= 4.55/8.20 = 0.56$.
The feed enters on the $(0.56)(31) = $ 17th plate from top.

10–6 PACKED COLUMN—H.E.T.P.

It is possible to equate the length of a packed column required to achieve a separation equivalent to one theoretical stage; *the height equivalent to a theoretical plate, H.E.T.P.* A general correlation in terms of operating parameters has been provided by Murch.[1]

$$\text{H.E.T.P.} = K_1 G^{K_2} d^{K_3} h^{1/3} \left(\frac{\alpha\mu}{\rho}\right) \tag{10–9}$$

[1] Murch, D. P., *Ind. Eng. Chem.*, **45**, 2616 (1953).

where H.E.T.P. = height equivalent to one theoretical plate, in.

G = vapor mass flow rate, lb/(hr)(ft²)

d = tower diameter, in.

h = packed height, ft

α = relative volatility of key components

μ = liquid viscosity, centipoise

ρ = liquid density, g/cm³

K_1, K_2, and K_3 are constants for the packing, given in Table 10–1.

TABLE 10–1

CONSTANTS IN EQUATION 10–9

Type of packing	Size (in.)	K_1	K_2	K_3
Rings	$\frac{1}{4}$			1.24
	$\frac{3}{8}$	2.1	−0.37	1.24
	$\frac{1}{2}$	8.53	−0.24	1.24
	1	0.57	−0.10	1.24
	2	0.42	0.0	1.24
Saddles	$\frac{1}{2}$	5.62	−0.45	1.11
	1	0.76	−0.14	1.11
McMahon	$\frac{1}{4}$	0.017	0.50	1.0
	$\frac{3}{8}$	0.20	0.25	1.0
	$\frac{1}{2}$	0.33	0.20	1.0
Protruded	$\frac{1}{4}$	0.39	0.25	0.3
	$\frac{3}{8}$	0.076	0.5	0.3
	$\frac{3}{4}$*	0.45	0.3	—
	1	3.06	0.12	0.3
Stedman	No. 128(2)	0.077	0.48	0.24
	107(3)	0.363	0.26	0.24
	115(6)	0.218	0.32	0.24

* Raschig rings of protruded metal.

To use this correlation we need to know the column diameter d and height h. As a first apppproximation the height can be estimated, since it enters into Eq. 10–9 to only the one-third power. Thus the design procedure consists of (1) calculating the number of stages (by the methods of Chapters 4, 7, or section 10–2); (2) estimating the column diameter from fluid flow consideration based on the specified throughput, G (detailed method to be discussed in section 10–7); (3) assuming a column height, h. We now calculate the H.E.T.P. by Eq. 10–9. The actual column height is equal to the H.E.T.P. times the number of stages. If the actual height h is substantially different from that assumed in step (3), the calculation is repeated.

10–7 PACKED COLUMNS—DIAMETER

To calculate the column diameter, information about the characteristics of the column packing to be used is required; particularly the flooding velocities, and allowable throughputs. Typical of the available correlations is Fig. 10–7, where

V_f = gas velocity in empty tower at flooding, ft/sec
G = gas rate, lb/(hr)(ft²)
L = liquid rate, lb/(hr)(ft²)
μ = liquid viscosity, centipoise
ρ_G = gas density, lb/ft³
ρ_L = liquid density, lb/ft³
a = area of packing, ft²/ft³ tower volume
ϵ = fractional dry voids in packing.

Values of a/ϵ^3 for various types of packing are given in Table 10–2.

EXAMPLE 10–2.[1] A distillation tower is required for the recovery of methanol from an aqueous solution containing 68.5% methanol by weight. The feed is saturated liquid at its boiling point. At the top of the stripping section the liquid flow rate is 880 lb/hr and the vapor at this point contains 84.0% of methanol by weight. (a) Calculate the flooding velocity for a column packed with 1-in. rings and estimate the minimum column diameter. (b) A McCabe-Thiele construction shows eight stages to be required. How high must the packed column be?

Vapor density at top of stripping section, $\rho_G = 0.063$ lb/ft³
Liquid density, $\rho_L = 54$ lb/ft³
Liquid viscosity, $\mu = 0.50$ cp
Relative volatility, $\alpha = 4$

Solution: The vapor flow rate at the top of the stripping section is calculated by means of a material balance, assuming that the loss of methanol in the water leaving the bottom of the column is negligible.

[1] From Norman, W. S., *Absorption, Distillation, and Cooling Towers*, John Wiley and Sons, 1961.

TABLE 10–2
PACKING CHARACTERISTIC a/ϵ^3

	Experimental value of a/ϵ^3, ft²/ft³		
Packing	Dry packed	Wet packed	Wet packed, shaken
Porcelain rings			
$\frac{1}{4}$ in.	768	593	844
$\frac{1}{2}$ in.	517	399	600
$\frac{3}{4}$ in.	199	187	249
1 in.	150	136	199
$1\frac{1}{2}$ in.	108	95	136
2 in	46	44	56
Carbon rings			
$\frac{1}{2}$ in.	373	317	396
1 in.	170	145	194
$1\frac{1}{2}$ in.	92	88	109
2 in.	56	51	63
Berl saddles			
$\frac{1}{2}$ in.	574	371	591
1 in.	229	169	246

Weight of methanol in liquid feed = $880 \times 0.685 = 602$ lb/hr

Vapor flow rate = $602/0.84 = 716$ lb/hr

The flooding velocity will be calculated using the Sherwood, Shipley, and Holloway correlation, Fig. 10–7.

$$\frac{L}{G}\sqrt{\frac{\rho_G}{\rho_L}} = \frac{880}{716}\sqrt{\frac{0.063}{54}} = 0.0422$$

From Fig. 10–7,

$$\frac{V_f a}{g\epsilon^3}\left(\frac{\rho_G}{\rho_L}\right)\mu^{0.2} = 0.15$$

The values of a/ϵ^3 for 1-in. rings are given in Table 10–2. The highest value (wet packed, shaken) will be employed, namely, 199 ft²/ft³. Then

$$V_f^2 = \frac{0.15 \times 32.2 \times 54}{199 \times 0.063 \times 0.5^{0.2}} = 24$$

(a) $\qquad V_f = 4.9$ ft/sec

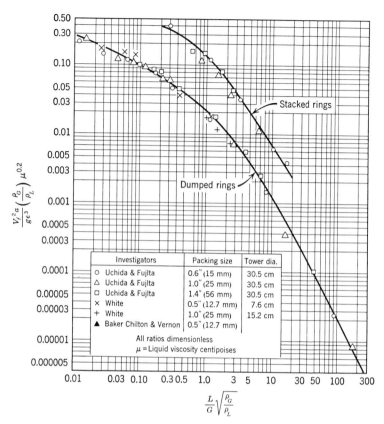

FIG. 10–7. Flooding correlation of Sherwood, Shipley, and Holloway. [From *Ind. and Eng. Chem.*, **30**, 765 (1938).]

For a conservative design, the maximum vapor velocity may be taken as 80% of the flooding velocity.

$$V_s = 0.8 \times 4.9 = 3.92 \text{ ft/sec}$$

$$\text{Vapor flow rate} = \frac{716}{0.063 \times 3600} = 3.16 \text{ cu ft/sec}$$

Cross section of tower = $3.16/3.92 = 0.81$ ft²
Diameter of tower = 1.02 ft

(b) By Eq. 10–9, H.E.T.P. = 0.8
Height of column = $(8)(0.8) = 6.4$ ft

10-8 TRAY DESIGN

The detailed layout of a tray is something which is generally left to fabricators who specialize in their construction.

Commercialized correlations which can be used to achieve operable designs for weirs, downspouts, and caps are to be found in Perry, *op. cit.*, Robinson and Gilliland, *op. cit.*, or Smith, *op. cit.*

eleven / stagewise calculations by calculus of finite differences

The solutions to stagewise contactor design problems have been seen to be in the form of discontinuous functions represented by straight line segments on x-y diagrams. It is apparent that this type of problem does not lend itself to solution by methods of differential calculus. In contrast, the calculus of finite differences is a mathematical tool well suited to the solution of problems involving discontinuous dependent variables of the sort encountered in stagewise calculations.

11-1 LINEAR DIFFERENCE EQUATIONS

Consider the case of the multi-stage contactor of Fig. 11-1 operating under conditions of constant mole or mass phase ratio. A material balance around each stage of the contactor yields the following N simultaneous equations:

Stage 1

$$VY_1 + LX_1 = LX_2 + VY_0 \qquad (11\text{-}1)$$

Stage 2

$$VY_2 + LX_2 = LX_3 + VY_1 \qquad (11\text{-}2)$$

.
.
.
.

Stage N

$$VY_N + LX_N = LX_{N+1} + VY_{N-1} \qquad (11\text{-}3)$$

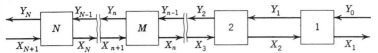

FIG. 11–1. Multi-stage contactor.

If the equilibrium curve, over the range of interest in the problem, is approximated by the linear relationship,

$$Y = KX \qquad (11-4)$$

additional N simultaneous equations can be written for the contacts in each stage of the contactor:

$$Y_1 = KX_1 \qquad (11-5)$$

$$Y_2 = KX_2 \qquad (11-6)$$

.

.

.

.

$$Y_N = KX_N \qquad (11-7)$$

In total, there are $2N$ equations to be solved for $2N$ unknowns. In an N-stage countercurrent contactor, there are $2N + 2$ streams; therefore if any two streams are specified, Eqs. 11–1 to 11–7 serve to define the remaining streams, and the problem is reduced to one of direct algebraic substitution (see, for instance, Example 1–1). This approach, however, involves a considerable amount of computation, particularly for multi-cascade systems. A substantial simplification of the equations can be achieved if we recognize the fact that the simultaneous equations describing the equilibrium and material balances are related through the multi-stage structure of the over-all system.

For stage n, we may write Eqs. 11–3 and 11–7 as:

$$VY_n + LX_n = LX_{n+1} + VY_{n-1} \qquad (11-8)$$

and

$$Y_n = KX_n \qquad (11-9)$$

Substitution of Eq. 11–9 into 11–8 yields

$$\frac{L}{K} Y_{n+1} - \left(V + \frac{L}{K}\right) Y_n + VY_{n-1} = 0 \qquad (11-10)$$

Letting $A = VK/L$, and rearranging,

$$Y_{n+1} - (A + 1)Y_n + AY_{n-1} = 0 \qquad (11\text{--}11)$$

Difference equations such as 11–11 relate properties on each side of a discrete stage. They are analogous to differential equations, which relate variables on each side of a differential increment in the independent variable, except that the increment is finite (in this case a finite stage).

11–2 PROPERTIES OF DIFFERENCE EQUATIONS[1]

Difference equations, such as Eq. 11–11, have many properties analogous to differential equations. If they are of the polynomial form

$$P_n(X)Y_{x+n} + P_{n-1}(X)Y_{x+n-1} + \cdots + P_0(X)Y_x = Q(X) \qquad (11\text{--}12)$$

where the coefficients P are functions of X, then

1. The solution of Eq. 11–12 is a polynomial of the form

$$Y = \frac{aX^n}{n!} + C_1X^{n-1} + \cdots + C_{n-1}X + C_n \qquad (11\text{--}13)$$

where the C's are arbitrary constants, n in number, and can be evaluated if n values of Y are specified for nX's.

2. If the difference equation is linear, with constant coefficients, the solution can be obtained as the sum of a homogeneous equation of the form

$$A_nY_{x+n} + A_{n-1}Y_{x+n-1} + \cdots + A_0Y_x = 0 \qquad (11\text{--}14)$$

plus a particular solution.

3. Substitution of $Y_x = C\beta^X$, a trial solution, yields an algebraic nth degree polynomial,

$$A_n\beta^n + A_{n-1}\beta^{n-1} + \cdots + A_0 = 0 \qquad (11\text{--}15)$$

which contains n essential arbitrary constants, and which may have real and distinct, real and repeated, complex conjugate, and/or repeated complex conjugate roots.

EXAMPLE 11–1.   One hundred fifty pounds of TBP are being used to extract uranyl nitrate from 90 pounds of water. The phases are

---

[1] Mickley, H. S., T. K. Sherwood, and C. E. Reed, *Applied Mathematics in Chemical Engineering*, p. 320, McGraw-Hill, 1957.

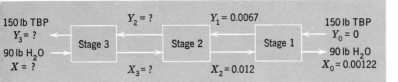

FIG. 11–2. Flow sheet for Example 11–1.

insoluble, and the phase equilibrium is $Y_n = KX_n$ where $K = 5.5$ (see Example 1–1, page 9). Analytical data about stage 1 is available. Calculate Y_2 and Y_3.

Solution: Basis: Flow sheet (Fig. 11–2).

Insertion of the trial solution, $Y = C\beta^n$, into Eq. 11–11 yields

$$\beta^2 - (A + 1)\beta + A = 0$$

which has roots at $\beta = 1$ and $\beta = A$. Substituting into the trial solution, and adding the two solutions of the linear difference equations,

$$Y = C_1 + C_2 A^n$$

Since A is equal to $VK/L = (150)(5.5)(90) = 9.17$, the constants C_1 and C_2 may be evaluated from the boundary conditions, obtained from the data given for stage 1 (Fig. 11–2).

$$Y_0 = 0 \qquad \text{at } n = 0$$

$$Y_1 = 0.0067 \qquad \text{at } n = 1$$

Hence, $Y_n = -0.00082 + 0.00082(9.17)^n$.

For $n = 2$, $Y_2 = 0.0684$. This result precisely checks Example 1–1. For $n = 3$, $Y_3 = 0.634$. The corresponding X's could be determined by material balances.

11–2 McCABE-THIELE CALCULATIONS BY CALCULUS OF FINITE DIFFERENCES[1]

If the equilibrium relationship is non-linear, but the relative volatility α is constant, the equilibrium curve

$$y_{n-1} = \frac{x_{n-1}}{1 + (\alpha - 1)x_{n-1}} \qquad (11-16)$$

[1] Ning Hsing Chen, "Analytical Solution for McCabe-Thiele Diagram," Aerojet General Corporation, Sacramento, Calif., December 1961.

When solved simultaneously with a material balance equation about a plate in the enriching section,

$$Vy_{n-1} = Lx_n + Dx_D \qquad (11\text{--}17)$$

yields the difference equation,

$$x_n x_{n-1} + ax_n + bx_{n-1} + c = 0 \qquad (11\text{--}18)$$

where

$$a = \frac{Dx_D(\alpha - 1) - V\alpha}{L(\alpha - 1)} \; ; \qquad b = \frac{1}{\alpha - 1} \; ; \qquad c = \frac{Dx_D}{L(\alpha - 1)}$$

$$(11\text{--}19)$$

Equation 11–18 is a Riccati, non-linear difference equation which may be reduced to a linear equation by translating the x-axis by a constant amount, δ. A detailed discussion of the method and a solution of Eq. 11–18 is given in Mickley et. al., *op. cit.*, p. 327.

The final equation for the enriching section is

$$\left(-\frac{a + x_i}{b + x_i}\right)^n = \frac{(x_D - x_i)(a + b + x_i + x_n)}{(x_n - x_i)(a + b + x_i + x_D)} \qquad (11\text{--}20)$$

where

$$x_i = \frac{-(a + b) - \sqrt{(a + b)^2 - 4c}}{2} \qquad (11\text{--}21)$$

Equations 11–20 and 11–21 incorporate the boundary condition, $x_n = x_D$, when $n = 0$. The x_i in Eq. 11.21 is the same x_i obtained by the quadratic formula solution of Eq. 11–18. Hence it marks the intersection of the operating and equilibrium lines, or, if this is not known, the intersection of the q line with the operating line,

$$x_{iq} = \frac{x_F + (q - 1)(1 - L/V)x_D}{q - (q - 1)L/V} \qquad (11\text{--}22)$$

will give us the second boundary condition needed to solve a problem.

Similar equations may be developed for the stripping section (Chen, *op. cit.*).

problems

For Chapter 1:

1–1. Using the table of properties obtained from a handbook, discuss what unit operations might be used to separate mixtures of (*a*) propane and methane, (*b*) acetylene and ethylene, (*c*) hydrogen and deuterium, (*d*) *o*-xylene and *p*-xylene, (*e*) asphalt and nonasphaltic oil, (*f*) calcium and strontium-90, (*g*) aromatic and non-aromatic hydrocarbons, (*h*) styrene (mw 10,000) and styrene (mw 100,000), (*i*) water and NaCl.

1–2. The distribution of ethanol, *E*, between water, *W*, and ester, *S*, is roughly 2 = (mole fr. *E* in *S*)/(mole fr. *E* in *W*) = y/x at 20°C. A 10 percent mole fraction solution of *E* in *W* is to be extracted with *S* to recover the ethanol. Compare the separations to be obtained in a one-stage countercurrent, co-current, and cross flow contactor with various ratios of *S* to *W*. Repeat the calculation for two stages, three stages, and infinite stages.

   (*b*) Repeat the calculations assuming the equilibrium data were represented by the equation $y = (2x)/(1 + x)$.

1–3. The uranyl nitrate in two tons of a 20 weight percent uranyl nitrate in water solution is to be extracted with 500 pounds of tributyl phosphate. Compare the percentage recovery for the following alternative procedures (for equilibrium data see Example 1–1).

   (*a*) A single stage batch extraction.

   (*b*) Three batch extractions with one-third of the total solvent used in each batch (the solvent is withdrawn after contacting the entire *UN* phase).

   (*c*) A two-stage co-current extraction.

   (*d*) A three-stage countercurrent extraction.

   (*e*) An infinite stage countercurrent extraction.

1–4. Prior to liquefaction, air is dried by contacting it with a silica gel adsorbent. The air entering the drier with 0.003 lb water/lb dry air must be dried to a minimum water content of 0.0005. Using the equilibrium data below, calculate the lb gel per lb dry air required for the following:

(a) A single stage batch contactor.

(b) A two stage countercurrent column.

(c) A two stage crossflow contactor with equally divided adsorbent flows.

$\dfrac{\text{lb } H_2O}{\text{lb dry air}}$	0.00016	0.0005	0.001	0.0015	0.002	0.0025	0.003
$\dfrac{\text{lb } H_2O}{\text{lb gel}}$	0.012	0.029	0.044	0.060	0.074	0.086	0.092

Data from Eagleton, L. C., and H. Bliss, *Chem. Eng. Prog.* **49**, 543 (1953).

FOR CHAPTER 2:

2-1. In the air drying of solid, two situations can arise:

(1) A free liquid (water) phase may be present, as for example, in the drying of a floatation mixture.

(2) The water is not present as a separate phase, as for example, in the drying of moist wood or leather.

For the two cases, (1) and (2), indicate all possible phase equilibrium relationships by labelling the ordinate and abscissas on blank graphs. Consider a plot of T versus P to be the same as a plot of P versus T. Indicate which of the following variables must be held constant (if any). Also use the nomenclature indicated.

P pressure x_w concentration of water in the solid phase

T temperature y_w concentration of water in the gas phase

                       x_s concentration of inert in the solid phase

                       y_a concentration of air in the gas phase

Assume that the solid has no vapor pressure. Label the phases.

2-2. An amount of solvent in excess of that required to dissolve all of solute A out of a solid solution of A plus B is used in a leaching operation. The total possible number of equilibrium phase diagrams is ———.

2-3. A liquid mixture containing 25 mole percent benzene and 75 mole percent alcohol is heated at constant pressure of 1 atmosphere from a temperature of 60°C to 90°C. Benzene and ethanol are miscible in all proportions.

(a) At what temperature does vaporization begin?

(b) What is the composition of the first bubble of equilibrium vapor formed?

(c) What is the composition of the residual liquid when 25 mole percent has evaporated? Assume that all vapor formed is retained within the apparatus and that it is completely mixed and in equilibrium with the residual liquid.

(d) Repeat part (c), for 90 mole percent vaporized.

(e) Repeat part (d), if after 25 mole percent vaporized as in part (c) this vapor was removed and an additional 35 mole percent were vaporized by the same technique used in part (c).

(f) Plot the temperature versus the percent vaporized for parts (d) and (e).

Use the vapor pressure data below in conjunction with Raoult's law to construct a T-x-y curve. Compare your T-x-y diagram and the answers obtained in (a-f) with those obtained using the experimental T-x-y data.

Vapor Pressures, mm Hg

	20	40	60	100	200	400	760
Ethanol	8	19.0	26.0	34.9	48.4	63.5	78.4
Benzene	−2.6	7.6	15.4	26.1	42.2	60.6	80.1

(temperatures in °C)

Experimental x-y Data

Temperature	78.4	77.5	75	72.5	70	68.5	67.7	68.5	72.5	75	77.5	80.1
Vapor	0	7.5	28	42	54	60	68	73	82	88	95	100
Liquid	0	1.5	5	12	22	31	68	81	91	95	98	100

(mole percent benzene)

2–4. The relative volatility, α, of benzene to toluene is 2.5. Construct an x-y curve for this system at one atmosphere. Repeat the calculation using vapor pressure data (see Problem 2–3 for benzene data).

(a) What is the composition of the initial vapor if a 40 mole percent benzene solution is vaporized?

(b) If one-half of the solution in (a) were vaporized, what would be the composition of the remaining vapor and liquid?

(c) Compare your results with the data in Problem 4–9.

Vapor Pressure, mm Hg

	20	40	60	100	200	400	760
Toluene	18.4	31.8	40.3	51.9	69.5	89.5	110.0

(temperatures in °C)

2–5. A mixture of chloroform ($CHCl_3$) and acetic acid at 18°C is to be extracted with water to recover the acid.

(a) One hundred lbs of a mixture containing 35 wt percent $CHCl_3$ and 65 wt percent acid is treated with 50 lb of water at 18°C in a simple, one-stage batch extraction. What are the compositions and weights of the raffinate and extract layers produced? Construct an equilateral diagram and solve this problem using it.

(b) If the *raffinate* layer from the above treatment is extracted again with $\frac{1}{2}$ its weight of water, what will be the compositions and weights of the new layers?

(c) If all the water is removed from this final raffinate layer, what will its composition be?

(d) Repeat the problem using the rectangular type diagrams of Fig. 2–6B and 2–6C.

EQUILIBRIUM DATA

SYSTEM $CHCl_3$—H_2O—CH_3COOH
Temperature 18°C

Heavy Phase (wt %)			Light Phase (wt %)		
$CHCl_3$	H_2O	CH_3COOH	$CHCl_3$	H_2O	CH_3COOH
99.01	0.99	0.00	0.84	99.16	0.00
91.85	1.38	6.77	1.21	73.69	25.10
80.00	2.28	17.72	7.30	48.58	44.12
70.13	4.12	25.75	15.11	34.71	50.18
67.15	5.20	27.65	18.33	31.11	50.56
59.99	7.93	32.08	25.20	25.39	49.41
55.81	9.58	34.61	28.85	23.28	47.87

2-6. Equilibrium data for the system acetone-air-water are given as:

y, mole fraction acetone in air	0.004	0.008	0.014	0.017	0.019	0.020
x, mole fraction acetone in water	0.002	0.004	0.006	0.008	0.010	0.012

(a) Plot the data as (1) a graph of moles acetone/mole air versus moles acetone/mole water, (2) partial pressure of acetone versus acetone/g water, (3) y versus x.

(b) If 20 moles of gas containing 0.015 mole fraction acetone is brought into contact with 15 moles of water in an equilibrium stage, what would be the composition of the discharge streams? Solve graphically.

2-7. Using the vapor-liquid equilibrium data of Problem 4-9, and the thermal data provided below, construct a H-x-y diagram for benzene-toluene. Make any assumption necessary.

	Benzene	Toluene
H_v =	103.57 cal/g at 25°C	98.55 cal/g at 25°C
H_v =	94.14 cal/g at 80.1°C	86.8 cal/g at 110°C
C_p (liquid) =	0.419 cal/g °C	0.440 cal/g °C

A 30 mole percent solution is at saturation temperature. It is fed into a one-stage still. What is the maximum heat load on the product condenser per mole of feed, if the product is subcooled 10°C?

2-8. One hundred pounds of a solution containing 0.3 wt fraction glycol in water is to be extracted with furfural. Calculate (a) minimum quantity of solvent, (b) maximum quantity of solvent, (c) the weights of solvent-free extract and raffinate for 100 lb solvent and the percent acetone extracted, (d) the maximum possible purity of glycol in the finished extract and the maximum purity of water in the raffinate. Use both Fig. 2-6A and 2-6B for solutions (after Treybal, *Liquid Extraction*, p. 129, McGraw-Hill, 1951).

FOR CHAPTER 3:

3-1. A gas absorption column to handle 800 lb/hr is being designed. An analysis of the pressure drop and pumping requirements shows that the maximum vapor velocity must not exceed 2 ft/sec. If the density of the vapor is 0.05 lb/cu ft, what is the column diameter?

Discuss, qualitatively, the factors governing the height of the column.

3-2. It is required to separate the indicated feed into the indicated products. Draw a simple block diagram showing a practical sequence of unit operations to accomplish the required results. State briefly the reasons for your choice.

Feed	Products
45% alcohol	1. 98% alcohol, 2% B
45% organic solvent B	2. 98% organic solvent B containing 2% alcohol
10% soluble non-volatile wax	3. soluble wax in solvent B

Properties

Boiling pt. alcohol = 120°C
Boiling pt. org. solv. B = 250°C

similar to

Viscosity of soluble wax at 10% conc. water
Viscosity of soluble wax at 50% conc. heavy motor oil
The alcohol is significantly soluble in water.
The organic solvent B and water are essentially completely immiscible.
The non-volatile wax is insoluble in water.

3–3. A new type of bubble cap called the siphon cap is under development at Stevens Institute of Technology (L. Cantiveri, Standard Oil (N. J.),

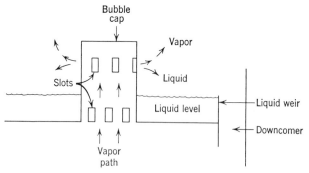

FIG. P3–3. The siphon cap, Problem 3–3.

patent pending). It is shown in Fig. P3–3. Discuss the operation of this cap, and compare it to the equipment shown in Figs. 3–6 and 3–7.

3–4. In the manufacture of synthetic rubber, a low molecular weight wax-like fraction is obtained as a byproduct. This byproduct is formed in solution in the reaction solvent. The reaction solvent is pure heptane. The byproduct has a negligible volatility. Indicate which of the following unit operations would be practical for the recovery of the solvent and why. Indicate why the others are unsuitable.

(a) Fractional distillation.

(b) Evaporation.

(c) Filtration.

FOR CHAPTER 4:

4-1. A saturated liquid mixture of benzene and toluene is to be continuously distilled at atmospheric pressure to produce a distillate containing 90 mole percent benzene, with a yield of 25 moles distillate per 100 moles of feed. The feed contains 69.4 mole percent benzene and will be fed continuously to a steam heated still. Residue is to be withdrawn continuously from the still, in which the agitation of boiling produces complete mixing. The vapors from the still pass directly to the top of a partial condenser and the partial condensate from the liquid separator following the condenser is returned to the still as reflux. Vapors from the separator, which are in equilibrium with the liquid reflux, are sent to a total condenser and are continuously withdrawn as distillate.

At equilibrium the mole ratio of benzene to toluene in the vapor may be taken as equal to 2.5 times the mole ratio of benzene to toluene in the liquid. Calculate analytically the total moles of vapor generated in the still per 100 moles of feed.

4-2. A plant has a batch of 100 moles of a liquid mixture containing 20 mole percent benzene and 80 mole percent chlorobenzene, and it is desired to rectify this mixture at 1 atm to obtain bottoms containing only 0.1 mole percent benzene. The relative volatility may be assumed constant at 4.13. There are available a suitable still and a column containing the equivalent of 4 perfect plates. The run is to be made at total reflux. While the steady state is being approached, a finite amount of distillate is held in a reflux trap. When the steady state is reached, the bottoms contain 0.1 mole percent benzene. With this apparatus, what yield of bottoms can be obtained? The holdup of the column is negligible compared to that in the still and in the reflux trap. Solve analytically.

4-3. The McCabe-Thiele diagram (Fig. P4-3) on the next page refers the usual distillation column. What is the significance of x_i (algebraic value and physical significance)?

4-4. A distillation column having 8 stages (7 + reboiler) is being used to separate a satd. liquid feed containing 50% A into a product stream containing 90% A. The liquid to vapor ratio at the top plate is

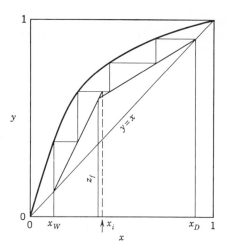

FIG. P4–3. Flow sheet for Problem 4–3.

0.75. The saturated liquid feed is introduced on plate 5, 100 moles / hr being the feed rate. Assume constant phase ratio.

(a) What is the composition of the bottoms?

(b) The L/V ratio in the stripping section is?

(c) The moles of bottoms/hour are?

Unbeknown to the operators, the bolts holding plates 5, 6, and 7 rust through, and the plates fall into the still pot. If no adjustments in steam, water, and feed rates are made, what is the new composition of the bottoms?

It is suggested that, instead of returning reflux to the top plate, an equivalent amount of liquid product from another column be used as reflux. If this product contains 80% A, what now is the composition of the (a) Distillate? (b) Bottoms?

Equilibrium Data

y	0.19	0.37	0.5	0.62	0.71	0.78	0.84	0.9	0.94
x	0.1	0.2	0.3	0.4	0.5	0.6	0.7	0.8	0.9

4–5. Solve Problem 1–4 graphically.

4–6. A saturated liquid feed stream containing 40 mole percent hexane, 60 mole percent octane, is fed to a plate column. A reflux ratio (L/D) equal to 0.5 is maintained at the top of the column. An overhead product of 0.95 mole fraction H is required and the column bottoms is to be 0.05 mole fraction H. A cooling coil submerged in the liquid of the second plate from the top removes sufficient heat to condense 50 mole percent of the vapor rising from the third plate from the top. (x-y data are given in Fig. 2–3.)

(a) Derive the equations needed to locate the operation lines.

(b) Locate the operating lines and determine the required number of theoretical plates if the optimum feed plate location is used.

4–7. The exit gas from an alcohol fermenter consists of an air-carbon dioxide mixture containing 10 mole percent carbon dioxide. This carbon dioxide is to be absorbed in a 5.0N solution of triethanolamine. The entering amine solution contains 0.04 moles of carbon dioxide per mole of amine. If the column operates isothermally at 25°C, and if the exit liquid contains 0.8 times the maximum amount of carbon dioxide, and the absorption is carried out in a 10 plate column, calculate:

(a) Moles of amine solution/mole of feed gas.

(b) Exit gas composition.

Equilibrium Data (mole ratios carbon dioxide)

Y	0.003	0.008	0.015	0.023	0.032	0.043	0.055	0.068	0.083	0.099	0.12
X	0.01	0.02	0.03	0.04	0.05	0.06	0.07	0.08	0.09	0.10	0.11

4–8. A fractionating column equipped with a steam heated reboiler as shown on the accompanying sketch and a total condenser is operated continuously to separate a mixture of 50 mole percent A and 50 mole percent B into an overhead product containing 90 mole percent A and a bottoms product containing 20 mole percent A. The column has three theoretical plates and the reboiler is equivalent to one theoretical plate, making four theoretical plates in all. When the system is operated at an $L/V = 0.75$ with the feed as a saturated liquid to the bottom plate of the column, the desired products can be obtained. The system is instrumented as shown on the diagram (Fig. P4–8). The steam to the reboiler is controlled by a flow controller so that it remains constant. The reflux to the column is also on a flow controller so that the *quantity of reflux* is constant. The feed to the column is normally 100 moles/hr but it was inadvertently cut back to 25 moles/hr. What would be the composition of the reflux and what would be the composition of the vapor leaving the reboiler under these new conditions? Assume the vapor leaving the reboiler is not superheated. Relative volatility for the system is 3.0.

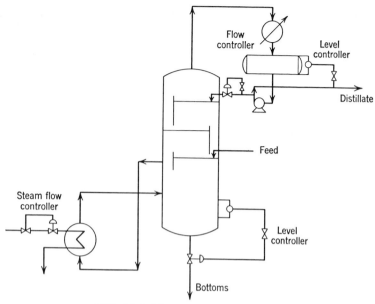

FIG. P4-8. Flow sheet for Problem 4-8.

4-9. A bubble-plate fractionating column containing eight theoretical plates, a reboiler equivalent to one theoretical plate, and a total condenser, has been in operation separating a benzene-toluene mixture containing 36 mole percent benzene at 1 atm. Under normal operating conditions, the reboiler generates 100 moles of vapor per hour. A request has been made for very pure toluene and it is proposed to operate this column as a stripper, introducing the 36 mole percent feed on the top plate as a saturated liquid, employing the same boilup at the still and returning no reflux to the column.

(a) What is the minimum feed rate of 36 percent material under the proposed conditions, and what is the composition of the liquid in the reboiler at the minimum feed?

(b) At a feed rate 25 percent above the minimum, what is the rate of production of toluene, and what are the compositions of product and distillate?

Equilibrium Data, Mole Fraction Benzene

y	0.21	0.37	0.51	0.64	0.72	0.79	0.86	0.91	0.96
x	0.1	0.2	0.3	0.4	0.5	0.6	0.7	0.8	0.9

4-10. A mixture of benzene and chlorobenzene containing 0.545 mole fraction of benzene at its boiling point is fed continuously to the bottom plate of a column containing two theoretical plates. The column is equipped with a still pot (heated by a steam coil) and a total condenser. Sufficient heat is supplied to the still to make V/F equal to 0.855, and the reflux ratio L/V in the top of the column is kept constant at 0.50. Under these conditions, what quality of product and bottoms (x_D, x_W) can be expected?

Equilibrium Data

x	0.100	0.200	0.300	0.400	0.500	0.600	0.700	0.800
y	0.314	0.508	0.640	0.734	0.806	0.862	0.905	0.943

4-11. A distillate containing 50 wt % alcohol, 45 wt % ether and 5 wt % water is obtained from the heads column of an isopropyl alcohol finishing unit. It is desired to recover the ether from this stream by extraction in a packed column with the water entering the top and the feed entering the bottom so as to produce an ether containing no more than 2.5 wt % alcohol and to obtain the extracted alcohol at a concentration of 25 wt %. The unit will operate at 25°C and 1 atm pressure. Calculate the theoretical stages required using McCabe-Thiele simplifying assumptions.

Equilibrium Data at 25°C and 1 atm

Isopropyl alcohol-Di-isopropyl ether-Water

Ether Phase			Water Phase		
wt % alcohol	wt % ether	wt % water	wt % alcohol	wt % ether	wt % water
9.3	88.6	2.1	11.7	1.6	86.7
24.9	69.4	5.7	17.5	1.9	80.6
38.0	50.2	11.8	21.7	2.3	76.0
45.2	33.6	21.2	26.8	3.4	69.8
5.0	93.6	1.4	10.2	1.5	88.3
2.4	96.7	0.9	8.1	1.8	90.1
3.2	95.7	1.1	8.6	1.8	89.6

Additional Points on Phase Boundary		
wt % alcohol	wt % ether	wt % water
45.37	29.70	24.93
44.55	22.45	33.00
39.57	13.42	47.01
36.23	9.66	54.11
24.74	2.74	72.52
21.33	2.06	76.61
0	0.6	99.4

4–12. A liquid feed stream containing 50 mole percent A is fed to the fourth plate (from top) of a six-plate column (plus reboiler). The liquid feed is sub-cooled to the extent of 20 Btu/lb mole.

The overhead product requirement is 95 mole percent A. The bottoms product is withdrawn from the fifth plate (from top).

(a) Determine the minimum reflux ratio $(L/D)_{min}$.

(b) For $(L/D) = 2.5(L/D)_{min}$ determine the bottoms product composition.

(c) What is the composition of the liquid phase in the reboiler?

(d) What is the product yield in moles/mole of feed?

Data and Notes

1. Latent heat of vaporization of A is 40 Btu/lb mole.
2. McCabe-Thiele simplifying assumptions apply.
3. The x-y equilibrium curve is defined by $\alpha = 2.5$.

4–13. A water-isopropanol mixture at its boiling point containing 10 mole percent of isopropanol is to be continuously rectified at atmospheric pressure to produce a distillate containing 67.5 mole percent isopropanol. Ninety-eight percent of the isopropanol in the feed must be recovered. If a reflux ratio, L/D, of 1.5 of minimum is to be used, how many theoretical stages will be required (a) if a still pot is used, and (b) if no still pot is used and saturated steam at 1 atm absolute is introduced below the bottom plate? What would the bottoms composition be in each case?

Vapor-Liquid Equilibrium Data

	Mole Fraction of Isopropanol at one Atmospheric Pressure							
°C	93.00	84.02	82.12	81.25	80.62	80.16	80.28	81.51
y	0.2195	0.4620	0.5242	0.5516	0.5926	0.6821	0.7421	0.9160
x	0.0118	0.0841	0.1978	0.3496	0.4525	0.6794	0.7693	0.9442

Composition of the azeotrope: $x = y = 0.6854$
Boiling point of azeotrope: 80.22°C

4–14. A solvent A is to be recovered by distillation from its water solution. It is necessary to produce an overhead product containing 95 mole percent A and to recover 95% of the A in the feed. The feed is available at the plant site in two streams, one containing 40 mole percent A and the other 60 mole percent A. Each stream will provide 50 moles per hour of component A, and each will be fed into the column as saturated liquid. Since the less volatile component is water, it has been proposed to supply the necessary heat in the form of open steam. For the preliminary design it has been suggested that the operating reflux ratio, L/D, be 1.33 times the minimum value. A total condenser will be employed. For this system it is estimated that the over-all plate efficiency will be 70%. How many plates will be required, and what will be the bottoms composition? The relative volatility may be assumed to be constant at 3.0. Determine analytically the points necessary to locate the operating lines.

4–15. An aqueous solution containing 10 mole percent of isopropanol is fed at its boiling point to the top of a continuous stripping column, operated at atmospheric pressure, to produce a vapor containing 40 mole percent of isopropanol. Two procedures are under consideration, both involving the same heat expenditure, i.e., V/F (moles of vapor generated/mole of feed) $= 0.246$ in each case.

Scheme (1) uses a still pot at the bottom of a plate type stripping column, generating vapor by the use of steam condensing inside a closed coil in the still pot. In Scheme (2) the still pot and heating coil are omitted and live steam is injected directly below the bottom plate. Determine the number of plates required in each case.

Equilibrium data for the system isopropanol-water are given in Problem 4–13. The usual simplifying assumptions may be made.

4–16. A still is charged with 70 moles of a methyl acetate-methanol mixture with composition $x_F = 0.445$ mole fraction methyl acetate. The column has the equivalent of seven theoretical trays, and boilup rate is 225 gal/hr, or in terms of distillate composition, $V = 25.2$ moles/hr. Determine the reflux rate-time relationship to get a constant distillate composition $x_D = 0.65$.

Assume molal latent heats of vaporization are equal and usual simplifying assumptions hold.

Equilibrium Data (mole fractions MeOH)

y	0.26	0.39	0.52	0.58	0.63	0.68
x	0.1	0.2	0.4	0.5	0.6	0.7

4-17. A mixture of maleic anhydride and benzoic acid containing 10 mole percent acid is a product of the manufacture of phthalic anhydride. This mixture is to be distilled continuously at a p of 100 mm, to give a product of 99.5 mole percent maleic anhydride and a bottoms of 0.5 mole percent anhydride. Using the data below, calculate the number of plates using an L/D of 1.6 times the minimum.

Vapor Pressure (mm Hg)-Temperatures (°C)

	10	50	100	200	400
Maleic anhydride	80.0	122.5	144.0	167.8	181
Benzoic acid	131.6	167.8	185.0	205.8	227

FOR CHAPTER 5:

5-1. A mixture of isopropanol and water containing 40 mole percent of isopropanol is to be distilled by a simple batch distillation until 70% of the charge (on a molal basis) has been vaporized (equilibrium data as given in Problem 4-13). What will be the compositions of the liquid residue remaining in the still pot and of the collected distillate?

5-2. Repeat Problem 5-1 for the case of a batch distillation carried out in a two-stage column with a reflux ratio of $L/V = 0.9$.

5-3. A 30 mole percent feed of benzene in toluene is to be distilled in a batch operation. A product having an average composition of 45 mole percent benzene is to be produced. Calculate the amount of residue, assuming $\alpha = 2.5$ or use the data of Problem 4-9.

5-4. Repeat Problem 5-3, assuming the operation is carried out in a three-stage still with an $L/V = 0.6$.

5-5. A distillation system consisting of a reboiler and a total condenser (no column) is to be used to separate A and B from a trace of non-volatile material. The reboiler initially contains 20 lb moles of feed of 30 mole percent A. Feed is to be supplied to the reboiler at the rate of 10 lb moles/hr and the heat input is so adjusted that the total moles of liquid in the reboiler remains constant at 20. No residue is withdrawn from the still. Calculate the time required for the composition of the overhead product to fall to 40 mole percent A. The relative volatility may be assumed to be constant at 2.50.

FOR CHAPTER 6:

6-1. A 0.25 mole percent isopropanol in water mixture is subject to flash vaporization. Plot, as a function of fraction vaporized, the composition of liquid and vapor leaving the separator. See Problem 4-13 for equilibrium data.

6-2. A 0.3 mole percent hexane in octane mixture is subject to flash vaporization. Plot, as a function of fraction vaporized, the composition of liquid and vapor leaving the separator, and the temperature in the separator (see Table 2-1 and Fig. 2-4 for data).

6-3. A mixture of benzene and toluene containing 60 mole percent B is being flashed in a continuous equilibrium still to yield a distillate containing 70 mole percent B. How much of this distillate can be produced from 100 moles/hr of the feed mixture, and what is the composition of the liquid product?

FOR CHAPTER 7:

7-1. A 0.5 mole fraction hexane in octane mixture having an enthalpy of 4000 cal/gram mole is (1) pumped from 1 to 5 atm, (2) passed through a heat exchanger, (3) flashed to atmospheric pressure. Sixty mole percent of the feed is converted to vapor in the process. Determine the composition of liquid and vapor leaving the chamber, and the total heat added (by the Ponchon method). See Fig. 2-10 page 30 for equilibrium data.

7-2. In Fig. P7-2, what is the significance of the lines $H_F - A$ and $H_F - B$?

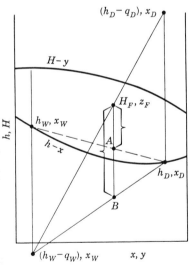

FIG. P7-2. Flow sheet for Problem 7-2.

7-3. A feed at 70°F, 1 atm, containing 50.0 mass percent ethanol and the balance water, is to be stripped in a plate column to produce a bottom product containing 1.0 mass percent ethanol. Overhead vapors are withdrawn as a distillate product.

(a) What is the minimum heat required per pound of bottom product to effect this separation?

(b) What is the composition of the distillate vapor for case (a)?

(c) If V/W at the still is 1.5 times the minimum and the Murphree plate efficiency (based on vapor compositions) is 70%, how many plates are required for the separation?

Saturation Temp. °F	Ethanol Concentration		Enthalpy of Mixture Btu/lb	
	Mass fract. in liquid	Mass fract. in vapor	Liquid	Vapor
212	0	0	180.1	1150
208.5	0.020	0.192		
204.8	0.040	0.325		
203.4	0.050	0.377	169.3	1115
197.2	0.100	0.527	159.8	1072
189.2	0.200	0.656	144.3	1012.5
184.5	0.300	0.713	135.0	943
179.6	0.500	0.771	122.9	804
177.8	0.600	0.794	117.5	734
176.2	0.700	0.822	111.1	664
174.3	0.800	0.858	103.8	596
174.0	0.820	0.868		
173.4	0.860	0.888		
173.0	0.900	0.912	9.66	526
173.0	1.000	0.978	89.0	457.5

Reference states for enthalpy = pure liquids, 32°F

7–4. An equimolal mixture of carbon tetrachloride and toluene is to be fractionated so as to produce an overhead containing 4 mole percent toluene and a bottoms containing 4 mole percent carbon tetrachloride. Calculate by the Ponchon method the theoretical minimum reflux ratio, theoretical minimum number of plates, and the number of theoretical plates when $L/D = 2.5$. The thermal condition of the feed is saturated liquid.

The assumption may be made that the heat content of the liquid and the vapor are linear functions of composition.

	BP (1 atm)	Average Specific Heat	Latent Heat of Vaporization
CCl$_4$	76.4°C	0.225 cal/gm °C	46.42 cal/gm at 76.4°C
Toluene	110.4°C	0.500 cal/gm °C	86.8 cal/gm at 110°C

Equilibrium Data (mole fractions CCl$_4$)

y	0.37	0.62	0.79	0.92
x	0.2	0.4	0.6	0.8

7-5. A mixture of 45 mole percent isobutane and 55 mole percent of *n*-pentane, at conditions such that 40 mole percent is vapor, is to be distilled into products containing only 2 mole percent *n*-pentane. The pressure on the system will be 3.04 atm absolute.

(a) Calculate the liquid and vapor enthalpies of isobutane and *n*-pentane mixtures, using liquid at 68°F as the datum plane, (zero enthalpy).

(b) Using these data, construct an enthalpy-concentration diagram and determine the minimum number of stages required to make the separation. *Data:* Equilibrium constants for isobutane and *n*-pentane.

$$P = 3.04 \text{ atm abs}$$

T	K_n	K_i
100°F	0.36	1.7
140°F	0.70	2.6
160°F	0.90	3.1
150°F	0.80	2.9
120°F	0.50	2.1
80°F	0.25	1.3
70°F	0.10	1.1

Boiling pt. at 3.04 atm: isobutane = 68°F, *n*-pentane = 165°F

Heat of mixing = negligible

Heat capacity of liquid isobutane = 0.725 × 10^{-3}t × 0.526 Btu/lb°F ($t = $°R)

Heat capacity of liquid *n*-pentane = 0.643 × 10^{-3}t × 0.500 Btu/lb°F ($t = $°R)

Latent heat of vaporization at boiling pt. (3.04 atm): isobutane = 141 Btu/lb; *n*-pentane = 131 Btu/lb

Average heat capacity of the isobutane at 3.04 atm = 27.6 Btu/lb mole °F vapor (over range of interest)
Average heat capacity of the n-pentane vapor at 3.04 atm = 31 Btu/lb mole °F
Assume heat capacity of mixture follows linear relationship.

7-6. A saturated liquid feed containing 40 mole percent hexane and 60 mole percent octane is fed to a distillation column at a rate of 100 moles per hour.

A reflux ratio $L/D = 1.5 (L/D)_{min}$ is maintained at the top of the column. The overhead product is 95 mole percent hexane and the bottoms product is 10 mole percent hexane. If each theoretical plate section loses 80,000 cal/hour, step off the theoretical plates on the Ponchon diagram, taking into account the column heat losses. (See Fig. 2–10 for H-x-y data.)

7-7. A mixture of acetic acid and water containing 50 mole percent water is to be separated into a distillate containing 90 mole percent water and a bottoms containing 20 mole percent water. A still consisting of a reboiler, a plate column, and a partial condenser will be used. Determine the minimum reflux, and using a reflux 1.5 times the minimum, calculate the theoretical plates. Assume linear H-x-y, and feed on the optimum plate.

If the Murphree efficiency is 85%, how many stages are required?

Equilibrium Data (mole fractions water)

y	0.17	0.3	0.42	0.53	0.63	0.72	0.79	0.86	0.93
x	0.1	0.2	0.3	0.4	0.5	0.6	0.7	0.8	0.9

Acetic Acid	Water
$C_p = 31.4$ Btu/lb mole °F	18 Btu/lb mole °F
$H_v = 10,430$ Btu/lb mole	17,500 Btu/lb mole

7-8. A fractionating tower is to operate as shown in Fig. P7–8. The system is benzene-toluene at 1 atm. There is no reboiler. The lower feed stream is introduced directly below the bottom plate, and the liquid from this plate is taken as bottoms product. Using the Ponchon method, determine:

(a) The reflux ratio (L/D) at the top of the tower, and the condenser heat duty.

(b) Rates of production of distillate and bottoms products.

(c) Total number of theoretical stages required.

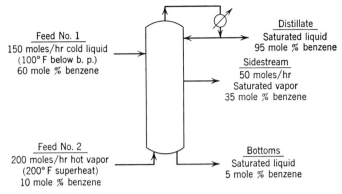

FIG. P7–8. Flow sheet for Problem 7–8.

(d) Optimum locations for introducing the upper feed stream and withdrawing the sidestream.

Thermal data are given in Problem 2–7.

7-9. An equimolal mixture of carbon tetrachloride and toluene is to be fractionated so as to produce an overhead containing 6 mole percent toluene and a bottoms containing 4 mole percent carbon tetrachloride, and a side stream from the third theoretical plate from the top containing 20 mole percent toluene. The thermal conditions of the feed and sidestream are saturated liquid.

The rate of withdrawl of sidestream is 25% of the column feed rate. External reflux ratio, $L/D = 2.5$. Using the Ponchon method, determine the number of theoretical plates required.

The assumption may be made that the heat content of the liquid and vapor are linear functions of composition. Equilibrium and thermal data are given in Problem 7–4.

7-10. Solve Problem 4–15 by the Ponchon method. Assume linear enthalpy concentration curves. The live steam is injected at 10 psig.

	Water	*Isopropanol*
$C_p =$	18 Btu/lb mole °F	0.522 cal/g °C
$H_v =$	17,500 Btu/lb mole	159.35 cal/g (at B.P.)

7-11. A feed stream containing 50% weight fraction acetone in water is to be extracted at 25°C in a countercurrent column with reflux to give a raffinate containing 12% acetone and an extract containing 55% acetone. Pure trichloroethane, which is to be the solvent, is removed in the solvent separator, leaving solvent-free product. Raffinate reflux is saturated. Determine (*a*) the minimum number of stages, (*b*) minimum reflux ratios, and (*c*) the number of stages for an extract reflux ratio two times the minimum.

System Acetone-Water-Trichloroethane 25°C

	Acetone wt. fract.	Water wt. fract.	Trichloroethane wt. fract.
Extract	0.60	0.13	0.27
	0.50	0.04	0.46
	0.40	0.03	0.57
	0.30	0.02	0.68
	0.20	0.015	0.785
	0.10	0.01	0.89
Raffinate	0.55	0.35	0.10
	0.50	0.43	0.07
	0.40	0.57	0.03
	0.30	0.68	0.02
	0.20	0.79	0.01
	0.10	0.895	0.005

Tie Line Data

Raffinate wt. fract. acetone	Extract wt. fract. acetone
0.44	0.56
0.29	0.40
0.12	0.18

For Chapter 8:

8–1. For the ternary systems given in Fig. P8–1, indicate whether
  (*a*) simple countercurrent extraction, *or*
  (*b*) countercurrent extraction with extract reflux, *or*
  (*c*) countercurrent extraction with raffinate reflux, *or*
  (*d*) countercurrent extraction with both extract and raffinate reflux
    would be expected to yield the most economical process.

8–2. Two solutions, feed *F* at the rate of 75 lb/hr containing 50% acetone and 50% water, and feed *F'* at the rate of 75 lb/hr containing 25% acetone and 75% water, are to be extracted in a countercurrent system with 37.5 lb/hr of 1,1,2-trichloroethane at 25°C to give a raffinate

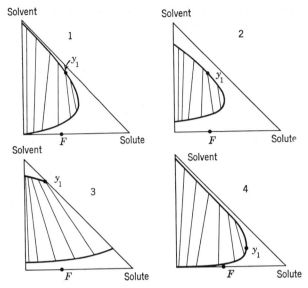

FIG. P8–1. Flow sheet for Problem 8–1.

containing 10% acetone. Calculate the number of stages required and the stage to which the feed F should be introduced (equilibrium data in Problem 7–11).

8–3. The extraction process shown in Fig. P8–3 is a multiple-feed countercurrent unit without extract or raffinate reflux. Feed F' is composed of solvent and solute and is an extract phase feed. Feed F'' is composed of unextracted raffinate and solute and is a raffinate phase feed.

Derive the equations required to establish the three reference points needed to step off the theoretical stages in the extraction column. Show the graphical determination of these points on a right angle triangular graph.

8–4. Solve Problem 7–11 on a right triangular diagram.

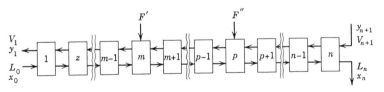

FIG. P8–3. Flow sheet for Problem 8–3.

8-5. Two liquids, A and B, which have nearly identical boiling points are to be separated by extraction with a solvent C. The data below represent the equilibrium between the two liquid phases at 95°C.

Determine the minimum amount of reflux that must be returned from the extract product and from the raffinate product to produce an extract containing 83% A and 17% B (on a solvent-free basis) and a raffinate product containing 10% A and 90% B (solvent-free). The feed contains 35% A and 65% B on a solvent-free basis and is a saturated heavy liquid. Determine the number of ideal stages on both sides of the feed required to produce the same end products from the same feed when the reflux ratio of the extract, expressed as pounds of extract reflux per pound of extract product (including solvent), is twice the minimum. Calculate the masses of the various streams per 1000 lb of feed. Solve the problem, using triangular coordinates, right triangular coordinates, and solvent-free coordinates.

Equilibrium Data

Extract Layer			Raffinate Layer		
A, %	B, %	C, %	A, %	B, %	C, %
0	7	93.0	0	92.0	8.0
1.0	6.1	92.9	9.0	81.7	9.3
1.8	5.5	92.7	14.9	75.0	10.1
3.7	4.4	91.9	25.3	63.0	11.7
6.2	3.3	90.5	35.0	51.5	13.5
9.2	2.4	88.4	42.0	41.0	17.0
13.0	1.8	85.2	48.1	29.3	22.6
18.3	1.8	79.9	52.0	20.0	28.0
24.5	3.0	72.5	47.1	12.9	40.0
31.2	5.6	63.2	Plait point		

(From McCabe and Smith, *Unit Operations in Chemical Engineering*, p. 802, McGraw-Hill, 1956.)

For Chapter 9:

9-1. Formulate a suitable series of independent variables for (*a*) a distillation column with two sidestreams, (*b*) an extraction with a sidestream and extract reflux (saturated), (*c*) two columns in series, the feed to the second being the distillate from the first.

9-2. The feed to a rectification tower consists of 20 mole percent ethylene, 10 mole percent ethane, 50 mole percent propylene and 20 mole percent propane. The desired overhead product and the bottoms are as tabulated below. The available cooling water temperature is such that is is estimated that the condenser outlet will be 100°F.

(a) What would be the tower operating pressure if the condenser were operated as a total condenser?

(b) What would it be if the condenser were operated as a partial condenser, with the overhead product being obtained as a gas? In this case, the reflux is assumed to be in equilibrium with the gaseous product.

(c) If tower operates with a reflux ratio of 2:1 ($L/D = 2$), what would be the composition of the vapor leaving the top plate, for part (b)?

	Feed Moles/hr	Overhead Product Moles/hr	Bottoms Moles/hr
C_2H_4	20	20	0
C_2H_6	10	10	0
C_3H_6	50	49.6	0.4
C_3H_8	20	1.6	18.4
	100	81.2	18.8

K Values, Temperature 100°F, Pressure, Atm

	15	20	25	30	35	40
C_2H_4	3.65	2.8	2.3	2.0	1.75	1.58
C_2H_6	2.55	2.0	1.67	1.45	1.3	1.17
C_3H_6	1.01	0.83	0.73	0.66	0.62	0.59
C_3H_8	0.92	0.75	0.65	0.6	0.56	0.54

9-3. (a) What would be the reboiler temperature for the tower described in Problem 9-2? The feed comes into the tower as a saturated liquid and the tower is operated with a partial condenser to produce a gaseous overhead product. Reflux ratio $L/D = 2$.

(b) What would be the composition of the liquid leaving the bottom tray?

(c) What would be the composition of the vapor leaving the second tray from the top of the tower?

K Values, Total Pressure 23 Atm

Temp. °F	100	150	200	300	400
C_2H_4	2.482	3.56	4.68	7.8	12
C_2H_6	1.78	2.50	3.38	5.8	8.9
C_3H_6	0.76	1.10	1.58	2.85	4.6
C_3H_8	0.69	1.01	1.37	2.49	3.96

9–4. A saturated liquid, 25 mole percent n-propane, 25 mole percent n-butane, 25 mole percent n-pentane, and 25 mole percent n-hexane, is to be rectified at a pressure of 115 psia to produce an overhead of 48.8 mole percent n-propane, 46.3 mole percent n-butane, and 4.9 mole percent n-pentane, and a bottoms of 46.0 mole percent n-pentane, 51.2 mole percent n-hexane, and 2.6 mole percent n-butane. Determine (a) minimum number of theoretical plates, (b) minimum reflux ratio, (c) for $L/D = 1.5(L/D)_{min}$, determine number of theoretical plates required, (d) solve parts (b) and (c) for thermal feed condition of 50 mole percent vapor.

Equilibrium data for the system at 115 psia can be found in Fig. 9–1.

9–5. A four component mixture having the (mole fraction) composition $C_3H_8 = 0.45$, $C_4H_{10} = 0.35$, n-$C_5H_{12} = 0.1$, $C_6H_{14} = 0.1$, is to be distilled at 200 psia. Ninety-nine percent recovery of C_3H_8 is desired. Using an average and constant α, and a reflux ratio of 2 moles/mole of feed, calculate the number of stages required by performing a plate to plate calculation.

For Chapter 10:

10–1. A multicomponent saturated liquid feed to a distillation column is

Component	x_F	α
A	0.04	2.8
B	0.15	2.0
C	0.32	1.8
D	0.40	1.1
E	0.09	0.9

The distribution of component C between feed and distillate is 0.85, whereas for component D it is 0.15.

Calculate the minimum reflux, minimum plates, actual plates, column diameter, plate spacing, column height, and feed plate location.

> Liquid density at b.p. = 40 lb/cu ft
> Liquid viscosity at b.p. = 0.34 centipoises
> Vapor density at b.p. = 0.052 lb/cu ft

10-2. For the column of Problem 4–18, calculate the actual plates, column diameter, plate spacing, and column height.

> Viscosity (feed) = 0.8 centipoise
> Relative volatility = 3.4
> Density liquid = 1.2 g/ml
> Density vapor = 0.000428 g/ml

FOR CHAPTER 11:

11-1. A 50 mole percent mixture of benzene-toluene is to be distilled to produce a product having 98% benzene and a bottoms containing 15% benzene. For $L/V = 0.75$, determine the number of plates in the enriching section for saturated liquid and saturated vapor feed. Repeat for $L/V = 0.4$, and check your results graphically.

11-2. The terminal concentrations in a ten-stage extractor system whose $\alpha = 2$ and whose phase ratio is 1 are $Y_0 = 0$ (at $n = 0$) and Y_{10} (at $n = 10) = 0.8$.

Calculate the X's and Y's for all intermediate stages.

index